Christ Over Cookies

Winning the War Between Feeding Your Face and Fueling Your Faith

Malaika Burley

CHRIST
over
COOKIES

**Winning the War Between Feeding
Your Face and Fueling Your Faith**

Malaika Burley

ISBN: 979-8-9881489-0-6 (pbk)

To the daughters of the Most High who are oppressed by their weight and the weight of it.

Contents

INTRODUCTION

How is it that someone can be living for the Lord, following His commandments, and yet be struggling so much with their weight? How is it that I could easily excel academically, in work, and in business, yet still end up weighing close to 400 lbs?

Gluttony is a sin. (This is where I'd insert the mind-blown emoji if we were texting each other.) But we already know that, don't we? We just aren't treating it as one. Gluttony is one of the most overlooked and least talked about sins in our churches. A lot of churches are even letting you do it right in the church building, and no one says anything about it. At least not to your face. Some will even make jokes about it from the pulpit to try to excuse it and make it seem like it's not a big deal. How can it *not* be a big deal when it's a sin? How can it not be a big deal to us as believers when sin is an offense against God? How can it not be a big deal when it is killing and oppressing so many of God's people? It's no laughing matter, and it's time that we start doing something about it.

I didn't grow up overweight. I was actually really thin. I started turning to food for comfort as a young adult. The more I got hurt by the very people that I wanted to love and accept me the most, the more I would eat and add on to my wall of weight. My wall became a way for me to reject others before they had a chance to reject me. My wall of weight became my defense. In reality, it turned into a prison. I was in bondage. I thought this wall of weight would protect me from getting hurt by others. The truth is I was hurting myself more than anyone else ever could.

After a few years of hiding behind my wall, I was tired of carrying the extra weight around. So I started dieting and trying to lose the weight I had gained. Only then I realized that I couldn't. Not for long anyway. I would try a diet, lose the weight, and then eventually gain it back. I would try another diet, lose the weight, and then gain it back again. This cycle just kept repeating itself and each time I would end up gaining back more weight than what I had originally lost.

I couldn't figure out what was wrong with me. I mean, I'm a good person. I love God. I think I'm pretty smart. So why couldn't I figure out this one thing? Why wasn't I smart enough to be able to lose the weight and actually keep it off for good?

Well, eventually I did figure it out. And you'd be surprised that it's not what you think. It's not about finding the perfect diet, because there isn't one. And it's not about just figuring out the best combination of macros and a calorie deficit. It's much more than that. It's deeper. And you're going to discover that as you dive into this book.

I want to share what has worked for me and what has helped me to lose over 80 lbs so far. At the time that I'm writing this, I'm still on my weight loss journey. But I haven't just lost weight, without dieting by the way, I've been able to keep it off this time. Keeping it off is what matters to me most. Keeping it off is what I couldn't do before. Keeping it off is evidence to me that I'm finally free. And through what we're going to uncover here together, you'll be able to lose the weight, keep it off, and finally be free too.

So why *Christ Over Cookies* as the title? Because my big problem was sweets. I had a major sweet tooth. I couldn't seem to control myself around them and they were a daily part of my diet. I've found through working with coaching clients and listening to conversations of others that struggle to lose weight that sweets and sugar tend to be what most other people have an issue with too. If sweets and sugar isn't a problem for you, this book and the principles in it apply to whatever *your* thing is.

Whether it's sweets, pizza, Chinese food, fried chicken, or chips. Whatever your thing is, this is for you. You know that one thing that you don't seem to have control with. My mom's peach cobbler comes to mind. That snack that you can't seem to eat just one of. That one food that always seems to make you go off your weight loss or health plan for the year. *That thing*. So, whenever I mention sweets, you just replace it with *your* thing.

Let's get into some Biblical principles and practical steps that have been working for me on my weight loss journey and that I know will work for you too. I want to share why it's been so hard for you to lose weight and keep it off despite all of your attempts. I'll explain why you've probably seen some success with weight loss but haven't quite hit the goal line yet. Finally, I'm going to give you actual steps and tools that you can use to help you be successful and mark ~~lose weight~~ off of your to-do list for good.

Chapter 1

WHY IT'S SO HARD TO LOSE WEIGHT

Why is it so hard to lose weight? Why is it so hard to stop eating sweets (or insert your favorite food)? Short answer...

Because sweets are delicious. Food is delicious.

I love food. I especially love going to a new restaurant and trying something that I've never had before. The atmosphere of the place, the presentation of the food, and the flavors of the dish all make eating food that much more pleasurable. And don't even get me started on the desserts. Food is delicious and we've created an entire culture and community around eating and enjoying it.

I'm not going to get into the ethics and morality of the food industry because that's another book for another day by another author. But food is purposely made to be delicious. The food industry (and your Nana) makes food in their special way so that it's good *to* you, not necessarily good *for* you. It's highly palatable and highly rewarding. Delicious food makes our brains and our tongues dance with delight. We like that feeling, so we want more of it. And more of it. And sometimes, more of it.

The short answer is that weight loss is hard because food is delicious. The long answer is much deeper and way more scientific. A part of that longer answer is that weight loss is hard because we've been deceived - by the enemy and by diet culture. Let's dive into that.

Food is a Gift

First off, I want to say that there's nothing wrong with food being delicious. It should be!

> *He gives food to every creature.*
> *His love endures forever. Psalm 136:25 NIV*

Thank You Lord for good food.

One of the reasons that God gave us food is for enjoyment, so it should be good. Last time I checked, He's a good God that gives good gifts (James 1:17). Actually, He gives the best gifts. Food is one of them, so we should enjoy it.

Another reason that God gave us food is for strength to carry out His will for our lives. Food is a source of energy. That's what calories actually are. It's the way we measure the amount of energy we get from food. Some foods are a healthier source of energy than others. Some foods will help us to have more energy for longer periods of time than others. Some foods supply us with energy plus nutrients that we need for other bodily functions. However, all food is a source of energy.

One of the reasons that we end up gaining weight is because we aren't using up all of the energy that we are consuming. When that happens, our bodies store that extra energy as fat. Our bodies are trying to save up the energy to use it later. But by the time we need it later, we typically end up eating more. We deposit more energy than we need without using up those energy reserves. In other words, we hold on to that fat and usually add more energy banks (more fat) to it later.

Food itself is a blessing from the Lord. My mom's peach cobbler might be a double blessing though. The Lord gave us food to enjoy and to have energy to do the things that He's called us to do. Yet we have been deceived.

Deception from the Enemy

The enemy knows that food isn't inherently bad, is supposed to benefit us, and is delicious. He uses that to his advantage to deceive us so that we fall into gluttony; and isn't it just like Satan to take something that the Lord meant for good and twist it around to make it work against us? Tell me if this sounds familiar.

Now the serpent was more cunning than any beast of the field which the Lord God had made. And he said to the woman, "Has God indeed said, 'You shall not eat of every tree of the garden'?" Genesis 3:1

He's basically asking Eve, are you sure that's what God said? Are you sure? He starts off by planting doubt, getting her to focus on lack, and causing her to question the instructions that the Lord gave them.

So when the woman saw that the tree was good for food, that it was pleasant to the eyes, and a tree desirable to make one wise, she took of its fruit and ate. She also gave to her husband with her, and he ate. Genesis 3:6

Satan twisted what the Lord said in order to deceive Eve into eating. Although the first temptation isn't really about eating, it's about the lust of the eyes, lust of the flesh, and the pride of life; I still don't take it lightly that eating and food was involved and was the means by which the sin was committed.

The enemy will take something that the Lord meant for good, in this case a boundary around this food, twist it, and tell us things to make us start questioning it. Is that what

God indeed said? Am I sure that's what God said? Is that what God meant this thing for?

That's how he deceives us. He starts planting these seeds of doubt by telling partial truths. He takes a little bit of the truth of God's word and adds a sprinkle of a lie to it, so it almost sounds right, but not quite. There's something off about it, but you just can't put your finger on it. Here's what I've come to realize:

A partial truth is a whole lie.

When it comes to the enemy, or anyone else for that matter, 99.9% truth + .1% lie = 100% lie. Let me tell you how he uses this same trickery with us.

Like I said before, food was given to us by God for enjoyment and strength to do His will and Satan will use that against us. Doesn't this sound just like something he would say? "God gave you food to enjoy. Then how can eating it be so bad? Eat what you want. When you want. Have as much as you want. God is good and everything from Him is good. So eat up!"

It *almost* sounds true. But is it? Of course not.

He wants you to continue to believe his lies, feeling like it's no big deal to eat and consume as much food as you want and to have as many sweets as you want. He wants you stuck in your weight and the weight of it. He wants you to feel helpless and hopeless. He wants you to forget that gluttony is a sin.

That's a part of what makes losing weight so hard. We have this food that is good and is meant for our good, but Satan is deceiving us into using it as a way to please our flesh and causing us to sin. Let's look at how he does that with another sin.

Sex is a good gift from God, but should be enjoyed within the parameters that He set for it. It is good within the context of marriage. That's the boundary that He set around it. Having sex outside of marriage is a sin. It's just a way to please our flesh and is no longer glorifying God when we do it. It's abusing the gift He's given us.

It's a similar situation with our food.

The problem isn't actually the sweets or that you're eating them. The problem isn't your favorite food or that you're eating it. The problem is that you're *over*eating it and the reasons behind *why* you're overeating it. When we overeat or overindulge, we're violating the boundary that God set around food. Eat and enjoy food, but don't overeat and overindulge. That's when it falls into the sin of gluttony.

That's how the enemy is deceiving us and using food against us. Before we take a closer look at this, there's another deception that needs to be addressed.

Deception from Diet Culture

Now the Spirit expressly says that in latter times some will depart from the faith, giving heed to deceiving spirits and doctrines of demons, speaking lies in hypocrisy, having their own conscience seared with a hot iron, forbidding to marry, and commanding to abstain from foods which God created to be received with thanksgiving by those who believe and know the truth. 1 Timothy 4:1-3

Satan has a way of twisting information, causing confusion, and leaving out important details so that you don't have the whole picture. He uses the diet industry and diet culture to do the same thing in order to capitalize on our struggle with weight and keep us bound. The industry tells us partial truths, distributes misleading information, and doesn't give you all the details you need to successfully lose weight and live a healthy lifestyle. They put out products, fads, and new diets with the premise of wanting to help; but underneath it all, they are like wolves in sheep's clothing. They come with the appearance of wanting to free you of your weight problem but are really just trying to sell their latest thing. They know you want to lose weight without much effort and sometimes at all costs, so they are using that to deceive you into buying their products or trying their diets. They'll even go as far as getting a doctor or celebrity to endorse what they're selling, because "hey, if doctor so and so says it's the truth, well then it must be".

As I said, the enemy is really good at deceiving us by leaving out vital information. He never clues us in to what we're fully signing up for when we believe his lies and fall for his schemes. I don't think Eve fully understood that by eating the fruit she would be banished from the garden and cursed for life. The diet industry tends to do the same thing. They leave out information about what it really takes to keep the weight off once you lose it or about the damage that their products or diets may cause you in the long run. For instance, they may flaunt a new diet that sounds really medical and based in science that will help us lose weight, but they leave out the part about how it'll wreck our kidneys if we do it. Or that part is in a very tiny print next to the words "results not typical". The enemy never clues you in to the full picture and neither does the diet industry.

Dear sister (or brother if you're reading this too), one of my missions is to help you break free from diet culture. I was bound by it too. It's this belief system that tells us we should focus on our physical appearance and being thin more than on our health and well-being. We are willing to try their diets, fads, and products, because we want to lose weight so badly. Usually what happens is that we try the diet or product and can't stick with it for very long. Then, instead of questioning *it*, we start questioning ourselves. We start asking, "What's wrong with me? Why can't I do this?". We try the latest fad and sometimes actually lose weight, but as soon as we stop the fad, we gain the weight back. Sometimes we'll even end up with a new health issue that the diet, product, or fad caused on top of the weight regain. The reality is that they don't really care about helping you become healthier. If they did help you become healthier, then you wouldn't need to give them your money anymore. They are just preying on the fact that a lot of us have a problem with our weight, want an easy way out of it, and will do almost anything to lose it.

The diet industry is not the health and wellness industry. These are two separate entities with two different agendas. One wants you to be whole, healthy, and thriving. The other wants your money, wants you to be dependent on them, and never be fully free.

But hey, maybe I'm wrong and I just have it out for the diet industry. Maybe all the products, diets, and fads will work for you, you'll lose the weight, and hit your goal. Even if that's true and you do lose the weight, you'll still have a large chance of gaining the weight back. That's because they are selling a quick fix or temporary solution to a deeper issue. It's kind of like taking medication to treat a symptom instead of actually curing the disease that is causing it. We've been deceived into treating the symptom, the extra weight, instead of addressing the underlying issue, why we're overeating in the first place. So let's look at the bigger issue here.

Chapter 2

WE'RE ONLY ADDRESSING A PART OF THE PROBLEM

The problem we have with losing weight and keeping it off is that we've only been addressing a part of the problem. That's what the diet industry and diet culture aren't telling you. And that's what the enemy doesn't want you to ever figure out. They want you to focus on the surface issue, the weight, and not what's going on underneath.

At some point, I decided I was tired of carrying around the extra weight. I was miserable. I didn't feel beautiful anymore. I didn't have energy to do day to day tasks. So I started dieting. I figured if I could just lose the weight, all of my problems would be solved, and I would feel good again.

I think I tried just about every diet out there or some form of it. I even tried a weight loss program or two. I've eaten cabbage soup, tried eating at a specific time, ate once a day, 6 times a day, low carb, high carb, drank weight loss shakes, and more. I even visited a plastic surgeon about possibly getting liposuction at one point. I would have short term success, but it wasn't sticking. The weight wasn't staying off, and I couldn't figure out what was wrong with me. Even when I was losing weight the right way by exercising regularly and eating better without dieting, I would still gain the weight back. But that's how we're supposed to lose weight. So why couldn't I keep the weight off even then?

For long lasting weight loss, there's more to it than what you eat and how often you move your body. That's only a part of the equation. Think about what typically happens around January 1st. How many people have *lose weight* or *get healthier* as one of their New Year's resolutions or goals? I know I used to write that down for years. It's a new year, and we're finally ready to start losing weight and stop overeating so we jump into action. We start changing our behaviors and doing more positive things for our bodies. And that's great!

But how is it going by the end of February? Most of us have quit by then. So simply changing our habits can't be the solution to sustainable weight loss. That's why previously I would try one thing after another, year after year, only to quit before reaching my goal. It didn't matter how much motivation or willpower I had on January 1st. I was usually back to the old habits and behaviors by February 15th. I didn't realize it back then that it wasn't just about what I was eating and how I was moving my body. Changing my habits to lose weight was only addressing a part of the problem I had. Lasting weight loss isn't just about the weight lost.

We Are More Than Our Bodies

And the Lord God formed man of the dust of the ground, and breathed into his nostrils the breath of life; and man became a living soul. Genesis 2:7

We are three part beings - spirit, soul, and body. So if we're three part beings, then it seems to make sense that we need to focus our weight loss efforts on all three parts of us. Having a healthy diet and exercising is only addressing one of our parts - the body. And to be honest with you, that's not even the part we should start with. It's really the last.

We are, first and foremost, spirit. We have a soul which is our mind, will, and emotions. And we live in a body. We are spirit with a soul in a body. I apologize for the simple diagram below, but I'm just using it to make a point. This is by no means an accurate representation of who we are.

SPIRIT   SOUL   BODY

Now because we are three part beings, we need to address the issue of weight loss with all 3 parts of self. We need weight loss tools for our spirit, our soul, and our body if we are to lose the weight, keep it off for good, and be free from the sin of gluttony. Dieting and weight loss methods we've used in the past have only been focusing on the body part of the equation. We're only losing the fat off our frame, but we have to look at the spirit and soul side of us as well. If we don't acknowledge our spirit and soul, then we are more likely to regain the weight back on our body despite our best efforts.

As I mentioned, we are, first and foremost, spirit. As believers, we are supposed to be spirit-led. Which means our spirit is leading the soul and body. We are born into sin, but once we accept Jesus Christ as our Lord and Savior our spirit is made new. We receive the Holy Spirit and are no longer slaves to sin and our flesh. We can now be spirit-led.

SPIRIT   SOUL   BODY
Proper Order

But we've been getting it backwards. We've still been allow-ing our flesh to take charge. We've been allowing our body and soul to lead, and the enemy wants us to keep it this way. He wants you to keep feeding your flesh instead of your spirit. This battle between flesh and spirit isn't a new one. You may be familiar with Apostle Paul's writings here.

We know that the law is spiritual; but I am unspir-itual, sold as a slave to sin. I do not understand what I do. For what I want to do I do not do, but what I hate I do. And if I do what I do not want to do, I agree that the law is good. As it is, it is no longer I myself who do it, but it is sin living in me. For I know that good itself does not dwell in me, that is, in my sinful nature. For I have the desire to do what is good, but I cannot carry it out. For I do not do the good I want to do, but the evil I do not want to do—this I keep on doing. Now if I do what I do not want to do, it is no longer I who do it, but it is sin living in me that does it.

So I find this law at work: Although I want to do good, evil is right there with me. For in my inner being I delight in God's law; but I see another law at work in me, waging war against the law of my mind and making me a prisoner of the law of sin at work within me. What a wretched man I am! Who will rescue me from this body that is subject to death? Thanks be to God, who delivers me through Jesus Christ our Lord!

So then, I myself in my mind am a slave to God's law, but in my sinful nature a slave to the law of sin. Romans 7:14-25 NIV

BODY　　**SOUL**　　**SPIRIT**

Out of Order

Paul is talking about this very struggle between spirit and flesh to lead. The struggle between being born a slave to sin and now being free in Christ Jesus and wanting to honor Him.

Surely, this is our battle with wanting to lose weight. We want to lose weight. We know that we'll be healthier and feel better. Yet we struggle with satisfying our flesh, the cravings, and just wanting to be able to eat what we want and when we want it. We want to quit overeating, but we can't quite seem to break free. We keep doing it. We want to stop, but we're having trouble stopping. Like Paul said, we keep doing the very thing that we no longer wish to do.

This is why willpower isn't the answer either. It's hard to will our flesh to fight against itself. We have to get to a place where we are spirit-led and things are back in proper order. So because of this, we can't just lose the weight off our body. We have to have a solution and tools for our spirit and soul as well. If we don't, we'll continue to satisfy the cravings and lusts of the flesh and just end up gaining the weight right back.

We're going to go over some Biblical principles and re-sources to help your spirit. We'll look at some mindset shifts and strategies for your soul. Then we'll take some practical steps for your body. Now when you're losing weight, you'll be addressing all three areas and will actu-ally be able to keep it off. Before we get into the strategy though, let's take a deeper look at some of the reasons why we're overeating in the first place.

Chapter 3
WHY ARE WE OVEREATING?

The enemy has been using deception to keep us operating out of order and wanting to continue to please our flesh. One of the ways he's doing that is by leading us to overeat. As I mentioned, it's not the food and eating it that's the problem. The problem is overeating it and the reasons behind why you're overeating it. Let's look at some of the reasons why we do it.

Emotions

One reason we tend to overeat is because of our emotions. Sometimes we turn to sweets when we're stressed, worried, sad, or disappointed. I've had many times when I was frustrated or heart broken and decided to overindulge on sweets because "I just don't care anymore". Or on the other end of the spectrum, we could be overeating as a way to celebrate. You're happy or joyous so you want to treat yourself. Most happy occasions and celebrations are centered around food and usually lots of it.

Habit

You may be overeating just because of a simple habit that you've formed over time. You're swinging by a coffee shop on the way to work, grabbing a coffee and a treat, and you've been doing that for the last 3 years. Or maybe it's through a fast food drive thru on the way home. Either way, you've established this habit and it's almost like autopilot when you pull in because it's just "what you do".

Let me give you an example of this from my own life. I tend to decide day by day what I want to eat. I don't necessarily like planning out my meals for the entire week and deciding what I want to eat for each day, because "what if I don't want to eat that thing on that day?". I know, it's an immature attitude, and I'm working on that. Anyway, my aversion to meal planning would inevitably lead to multiple trips to the grocery store in a week. At one point, it was a daily trip to the store. Well, our grocery store has these really delicious slices of birthday cake. You could buy them anytime you want, and you don't even have to be celebrating a birthday. What??!! So I did. And I created a habit that every time I went to the store I got a piece of cake. EVERYTIME. So that meant that some weeks it was 7 days of cake. It had become a habit. When I got more serious about losing weight, I decided to start making somewhat of a meal plan so that I wasn't going to the store as often. But when I did go, I would still get the cake. Go to that store, get the cake. It was a habit that would lead me to overeat.

Lack of Self Control

Lack of self control could be another reason you're overeating sweets. Someone brings in a box of donuts to work. It wasn't in your plan to eat any donuts that day. In fact, you had a quite satisfying breakfast. But the sight of the donuts alone, not to mention the smell because they are those hot fresh ones, is too much for you. You grab a donut. And sometimes another. And another because nobody's in the break room. Because of lack of self control, you go ahead and overindulge.

Addiction

Sugar addiction is a very real thing and can lead to overeating sweets. There have been many studies and research that have shown how addictive sugar is. And that also includes sugar substitutes, by the way. You may be overeating sweets because you are actually addicted to the sugar and your brain loves it. Some of us have addictive personalities or addiction that runs in our families. So your addiction may not be to drugs or alcohol, your drug of choice may be sweets or any other food.

Now that I've got your mind working with a few examples, think about times that you've overindulged on sweets or overeaten any other foods in the past. You didn't plan to do it, but it happened anyway. What was the reason that you overate? What were the thoughts or feelings you had prior to overeating? What were the circumstances that led you to overeat? If you can't think of any time in particular, then right down some guesses on why you believe other people overindulge on sweets. List some below.

_____

_____

_____

_____

_____

_____

_____

_____

_____

Now look back over the list you wrote down about why you or other people may overeat. When I look back over the ones I mentioned, emotions, habit, lack of self control, addiction, and reflect on some of the reasons I hear from coaching clients, the majority of the time it boils down to one thing.

We're putting our sweets in God's seat!

Have we gotten to a point where we're craving the sweets (or whatever your food of choice is) more than we are craving the Lord? The Lord created us to love, to desire, to crave, and to worship. But the thing is, we're supposed to love, to desire, to crave, to worship *Him*.

We are designed to turn back to Him for what we are longing for, not to our food. Has our desire for sweets turned them into an idol? I certainly didn't think I was idolizing sweets, but then I had to look back at the reasons that I was overeating.

One of the reasons I mentioned that people, including myself, might overeat is because of emotions. If you're eating sweets because you're stressed, heart broken, sad, or whatever the emotion is, then those sweets have become an idol. You're turning to the sweets when you should be turning to the Lord. He's the one that will give you peace and rest and can heal your broken heart. I know this may be hard to hear, but it was the reality check that I needed to start making a change. Remember, I've been there too and still have to check myself at times.

I also mentioned that overeating may have formed out of habit. Well, some habits are better to have than others. So ask yourself, is this habit serving me and God's temple? Remember our bodies are the temple of the Holy Spirit, and they are not our bodies to do with as we please.

> *Or do you not know that your body is the temple of the Holy Spirit who is in you, whom you have from God, and you are not your own? For you were bought at a price; therefore glorify God in your body and in your spirit, which are God's. 1 Corinthians 6:19-20*

Is the habit that we are continuing to do desecrating and destroying God's temple? Is it glorifying Him or simply pleasing our fleshly desires?

If lack of self control is the reason you're overeating, then the Fruit of the Spirit, self control, needs to be developed more. If overeating is because of addiction, then we need to turn to God to break free from the chains of that addiction.

Take a moment and reflect on why you overeat or overindulge. Are you desiring, craving, or lusting after sweets more than God's Word? Have you put sweets or any food on the throne of your heart where the Lord is supposed to be? If so, repent for the sins of gluttony and idolatry. Accept God's grace and forgiveness. And don't allow the enemy, not even for a second, to make you feel shame or condemnation for it. Let's talk about how we can make a change and move forward in freedom.

Chapter 4

WHAT CAN I DO ABOUT IT?

Gluttony seems to be the most acceptable sin in our society. In fact, some pretend that it's not even a sin and we often do it right in church. At least that's the case here in the South in the United States. We're willing to call Jesus Savior and make Him Lord over our lives, but it seems that we forget that includes Lord over our plates too. Gluttony, by the way, is not just about overeating. You can overindulge, have excess, and be a glutton of things other than food. But our focus here is food, sweets in particular.

We are struggling in this area of gluttony. Most churches aren't talking about it and some are just laughing it off. Have you been to a church potluck or fellowship dinner and hear prayers like, "Lord take the calories away"? Or maybe your church has coffee and donuts before service and someone will chime in "Oh, the diet starts tomorrow". I know we want to enjoy the food that God has given us, and we should, but we can't laugh off the fact that studies have shown that as a church, the body of Christ, we are some of the heaviest people in America[1]. Plus like I mentioned, gluttony is a sin. It is an offense against God. A lot of us in the body of Christ are struggling with it, and it's time we do something about it.

I think what happens is that some people get into this mindset of it being a "lesser" sin. They believe that because it's not harming anyone else or breaking any laws that it's not that big of a deal. Gluttony is seen as not being as serious as being addicted to alcohol or drugs or sex. We believe that we can stop and change our gluttonous behavior at any time. If that's true though, then why aren't we? The enemy is using that lie to continue to deceive us into thinking it's no big deal so that we stay bound and continue to sin. And any sin or any thing that has a hold of us is not ok.

> *All things are lawful for me, but all things are not helpful. All things are lawful for me, but I will not be brought under the power of any. 1 Corinthians 6:12*

We need to get to a place where we realize that and address gluttony for the real problem that it is.

Please know that none of this is coming from a place of condemnation. I was there before too. Making the stupid jokes and closing in on 400 lbs myself. I'm sharing this in love and because I want us to open our eyes to the problem that gluttony is and the deception of the enemy. Also remember that everyone struggles with something. Our issue just happens to be with overeating sweets or food. I get enraged at the enemy when I see how he is deceiving God's people in this area. I want us to be free from the oppression of being overweight and the weight of it. So sister (and brother) no condemnation here, just love. Don't allow the enemy to make you feel shame for this issue either. You picked up this book because you are ready to do something about it. Let's give the enemy two black eyes and break free from this problem together.

Now we're aware that we've been overeating and overindulging because we've been idolizing food and falling into the sin of gluttony. We also now know that just trying to lose weight isn't going to solve our problem because it's only addressing the body side of our being. Now let's learn what to do about it. I'm going to give you several Biblical and practical tools to help you conquer this problem for all three parts of you - spirit, soul, and body.

I believe that we should focus mainly on our spirit. We are spirit beings and our spirit can have the most influence over the soul and body when we strengthen it. "Strengthen" may not be the right word to use, mature is probably better, but I'm using the term strengthen. I like to think of my spirit getting stronger and bigger so that my soul and body seem small and weak in comparison. Now I know some of us ladies may not like the idea of bulking up. But trust me, we want our spirits shredded. (If you don't know, shredded means muscular or having well-defined or well-developed muscles.)

Remember that our goal is to be spirit-led. Our flesh is always going to try to take over, so we want to do what we can to strengthen ourselves spiritually. That's going to have a huge impact on our soul - mind, will, and emotions, and on our body. So let's focus on allowing the Spirit to increase within us. As believers, this should be the simplest for us. Simple, but not necessarily easy.

SPIRIT   **SOUL**   **BODY**

As I get into the tools for our spirit, soul, and body, I don't want you to get overwhelmed by all of the information. Focus on one thing at a time. Just one. I know it can be tempting to try to do them all at once. That can lead to an all or nothing attitude, and once you can't do it all, you end up doing nothing and are back at square one. Focus on one tool, master that, then pick another.

One thing I like to suggest to coaching clients is to pick the one that will serve you the most and best. That's the one that will have the biggest effect on your life. When you change that one, it may have a ripple effect on other areas. That's the one you start with. Then when you have a handle on it, open this book again, and pick your next tool to work on. Alright, let's go!

Chapter 5

TAKING YOUR SPIRIT TO THE GYM

He must increase, but I must decrease. John 3:30

Let's take our spirit to the gym- spiritually, of course. Like I mentioned, we want our spirit to be "stronger" than our soul and our body. That way we can be more spirit-led, as we should be, and less led by our flesh, mind, or emotions. There are four tools that I like to use initially for the spirit. There are more tools than these four, but these are ones you can get started with and pretty much implement on your own.

Prayer

Prayer is a tool that we should be using as a believer. I know, shocking right? So can I ask you a question? (I'm imagining you're nodding your head, yes.) Have you asked Holy Spirit, the Helper, to help you with this issue of overeating?

Most of us haven't because of the way we downplay or ignore the seriousness of this sin in our society and in the church. Or we haven't because we know if we ask He actually *will* help us and probably at that very moment that we really wanted that second cupcake. Holy Spirit is our Helper as it says in John 14:26, John 15:26, and John 16:7. As believers, His help is a huge advantage to us in our weight loss journeys that unfortunately unbelievers don't have. If we ask, He will help us in this area and we should welcome it.

And don't think that God doesn't care about you getting help with this or that it's a "small issue" for you to bring to Him in prayer. If He cares to number the hairs on your head (Matthew 10:30) then surely He cares about you living a healthy, thriving life free from the sin of gluttony too. So if you haven't yet, ask the Lord right now to help you. If you have asked Him before but didn't think of overeating as a sin back then, take a moment now to repent and ask God again for help.

If you're not sure what to say, I have some wording here. But just follow your heart, repent of your former sin, receive your forgiveness, and ask Holy Spirit for help.

Father God, thank You for this day. Thank You for Your love, grace, and mercy. Lord, I repent and ask You to forgive me for the sin of gluttony. Help me to turn away when I may be tempted to overeat sweets or food. Be my strength when I am weak. Remind me that my body is Your temple and that I should treat it well and glorify You with it. I thank You that Jesus died on the cross for this sin too and because of that I can be free from gluttony. Thank You for forgiveness and freedom. I receive it. In Jesus' Name I pray, Amen.

Again, don't get caught up too much in the words. You don't even need to say that much. You don't need to make it fancy, use big words, or a long prayer. Make it your own, as you feel led, and talk to your Father God, ask for Holy Spirit's help, and believe that you will receive it.

> *So Jesus answered and said to them, "Have faith in God. For assuredly, I say to you, whoever says to this mountain, 'Be removed and be cast into the sea,' and does not doubt in his heart, but believes that those things he says will be done, he will have whatever he says. Therefore I say to you, whatever things you ask when you pray, believe that you receive them, and you will have them. Mark 11:22-24*

When you pray for freedom from gluttony and help with temptation, or for anything else that is in alignment with God's word for that matter, you need to believe that you will receive it. One of the enemy's tricks is to make you think that your prayer isn't answered. He'll try to make you believe that your deliverance from gluttony or from food addiction didn't stick. But it did. It's just deception. Just because you're tempted by sweets or have a day when you overeat, doesn't mean that you weren't freed. When you pray for freedom from gluttony, do not doubt in your heart that you'll receive it. Believe that our good and loving Father will free you, and He will. It doesn't mean you won't have to ever struggle again, but believe and know that the battle is won.

And don't just stop praying there. Each day ask for help to walk out your freedom going forward. Prayer is a tool you get to use anytime. When you're faced with some-one bringing those unexpected donuts to work and you're tempted to grab one, ask the Lord to give you strength to walk away. If you're in the habit of swinging into the coffee shop on the way to work and want to change that, ask the Lord to lead you to a new, scenic route. If you're tempted to eat a pint of ice cream after a breakup, then pray and ask the Lord to heal your heart. His love is the best love anyway. Continue to use prayer to strengthen your spirit throughout this journey and in every area of your life.

Scripture

We are being deceived by Satan (and diet culture), and one powerful way we can fight that deception is with truth. We get to use the sword of the Spirit, the Word, scripture, to tear up the lies of the enemy. When you look at our armor in Ephesians 6, the Word is the one offensive weapon we carry. It's what we can use to strike down the enemy, tear down strongholds, and break those chains. When we look up the meaning of the Word of God in Strong's as it is referenced in Ephesians 6:17 , it is referring to the Rhema Word. Rhema is the spoken Word of God as opposed to Logos which is the written Word of God. As I'm reading scripture, the Lord will often give me a Rhema Word through His Logos Word, and He will do that for you too.

Remember when Jesus was being tempted in the desert by Satan. How did He defeat him? By using the Word of God. And let this blow your mind. Jesus is the Word made flesh. So the Word was speaking the Word! How powerful is that! We can also defeat Satan and strengthen our spirit with the Word, Rhema and Logos, as well.

> *And you shall know the truth, and the truth shall make you free. John 8:32*

You need to know the Word of God. You need to know the truth and allow it to make you free. The enemy is going to continue to try to steal, kill, and destroy you with his lies and deception, so pick up your sword. Let's take a look at a few verses and how you can use them.

> *All things are lawful for me, but all things are not helpful. All things are lawful for me, but I will not be brought under the power of any. 1 Corinthians 6:12*

This verse is a powerful reminder for us that while we may be able to eat sweets and enjoy food, those things should not have power over us. So when the enemy is trying to convince you to have more of that delicious sweet potato pie when you're already stuffed, let this verse be brought back to your remembrance.

> *Or do you not know that your body is the temple of the Holy Spirit who is in you, whom you have from God, and you are not your own? For you were bought at a price; therefore glorify God in your body and in your spirit, which are God's. 1 Corinthians 6:19-20*

Our body and our spirit is not our own. We don't get to do what we please with it. Well, at least we shouldn't. This is a great one to remember when you're debating on hitting snooze one more time instead of getting up and going for that prayer walk. I think you know what to do.

No temptation has overtaken you except such as is common to man; but God is faithful, who will not allow you to be tempted beyond what you are able, but with the temptation will also make the way of escape, that you may be able to bear it. 1 Corinthians 10:13-14

We all have been and will be tempted in this life. Temptation isn't sin, giving into it is. Thank God that He gives us a way of escape. Remember this verse next time someone brings those treats to the office that you weren't planning on having. Ask God to show you what you can do or have instead.

I speak in human terms because of the weakness of your flesh. For just as you presented your members as slaves of uncleanness, and of lawlessness leading to more lawlessness, so now present your members as slaves of righteousness for holiness. Romans 6:19

We were born slaves to sin and couldn't help ourselves before we accepted Jesus Christ as our Lord and Savior. But now we have a choice. Allow Him to be Lord over your life. Choose to honor Him with all that you do, including what and how you eat.

I've heard that many Christians don't take advantage of this powerful tool that we have and don't read the Bible because they don't understand it. That's what stopped me in the beginning too. I want to encourage you to start reading it on your own. Don't be comfortable with just reading your Bible on the big screen on Sundays when you're in service. If you want to strengthen your spirit, read it daily. Even if it's a devotional. Even if it's one verse. Just start.

> *This Book of the Law shall not depart from your mouth, but you shall meditate in it day and night, that you may observe to do according to all that is written in it. For then you will make your way prosperous, and then you will have good success.*
> *Joshua 1:8*

Reading your Bible, along with prayer, not only helps you to mature spiritually, but it draws you closer to God. It strengthens your relationship with Him. As you spend this time with Him, He will begin to speak to you through His written Word. He will give you instructions, ideas, and insights on your life and health journey. But He never has the chance to do that if you don't read His Word. Reading His Word also gives you points of prayer, because you can simply pray the scripture. This helps a lot when you're just not sure what to pray, and there's enormous power in doing it.

One of the things that really helped me to read the Bible more was realizing that Holy Spirit can't bring the Word to my remembrance if I never put it in my memory in the first place (John 14:26). I can't use it as a weapon against the schemes of the enemy if I don't know what authority and weapons I have. I can't pray the scriptures, if I don't know any verses to pray. I can't remind God of His promises to me if I'm ignorant of the inheritance I have in Christ Jesus. I had to read it first, so I could know and remember it later. As you read it, you will know and remember it and be able to use it for the weapon that it is.

Find a version that's easy for you to understand and then start reading. The King James Version may not be the one that resonates with you at first and that's ok. The King James Version still makes my eyes roll in the back of my head. You may want to start with the New International Version or the New Living Translation. Find the one that works best for you right now, and remember that you can switch up the version that you read at any time.

If you don't know where to start reading, the four Gospels are a good place - Matthew, Mark, Luke, or John. You could also try reading one Psalm or Proverb a day. Then from there, ask the Lord to guide you to what to read next. Before you start your reading each day, ask Holy Spirit to help you understand what you're reading and to reveal things to you as you read, then trust and believe that He will.

I also want to suggest that you have a journal with you as you read the Bible. This way you can write down those insights, ideas, and revelations that Holy Spirit is showing you as you read. It'll be a nice record to look back on as you strengthen your spirit and to see the promises that God has fulfilled for you over the years.

If you're interested in reading the Bible in chronological order and knowing on average how long it takes to read each book of the Bible, you can find that resource, as well as others, at ChristOverCookies.com/extras.

Fasting

Diet culture has taken the word fasting, twisted it, and watered it down. When most people think of fasting, they think of intermittent fasting or alternate day fasting as a way to lose weight. To most people fasting means dieting. But I'm not talking about dieting and weight loss here, I'm referring to fasting for spiritual strength.

You're not getting on the scale and seeing how much you weigh during a spiritual fast. It's not about that. When you are fasting spiritually as a believer, you're doing it as a means to strengthen your spirit and your relationship with God, to consecrate yourself, and to deny your flesh. Fasting is another way for you to allow Him (Spirit) to increase and you to decrease.

In general, Biblical fasting is having water only and no food for a period of time. It could be over multiple days or for a portion of the day. However, I'm going to suggest that you seek God and see how He leads you to fast when you do it. Ask Him how long you should fast and what you should give up. He's the one that will give you strength during the fast, so you should seek Him about it. Also let me take a moment to say keep in mind any medical advice that you need to stick to.

When you fast, your soul and your body are going to cry out for those sweets or that food. That's actually what's supposed to happen and you should expect it. That's when you're going to realize just how much sweets, and food in general, have power over you. But you know what? You're in control. Turn down the volume of your flesh and feed yourself some spiritual food.

> But He answered and said, "It is written, 'Man shall not live by bread alone, but by every word that proceeds from the mouth of God.' " Matthew 4:4

Fasting helps you to hear the Lord more clearly and the very nature of fasting helps you to strengthen your relationship with Him. That's because when you fast, during those times that you would normally eat physical food you should be indulging in spiritual food. During mealtimes, you're reading the Word of God, praying, and listening to Holy Spirit for guidance. Whenever the Lord leads me to fast, I'm always surprised at the strength I have during it. Let the Lord sustain you during your fast, not the local restaurant.

We can also see the importance of fasting when it comes to deliverance and being free from some of the strongholds and oppression that may be keeping you addicted to sweets. In Matthew 17, a boy was brought to Jesus to be healed and have a demon cast out of him. The boy's father had originally tried taking him to the disciples, but they couldn't do it. Jesus, of course, immediately set him free. When the disciples asked Jesus why *they* couldn't do it, He gave them two reasons. One reason was because of their unbelief or little faith, which we talked about when we discussed prayer. And for the second reason He says,

"However, this kind does not go out except by prayer and fasting." Matthew 17:21

For some things that we're struggling with, we need to utilize two of our tools, prayer and fasting. Fasting is a great spiritual discipline to implement into your life as a believer and a great tool for your spiritual toolbox. And you don't have to start off with a full fast for 40 days like Jesus and Moses. Pray and seek God on how He wants you to start.

It may be just for a half a day or it may only be abstaining from certain foods for a few days. Let Him lead you.

Fruit of the Spirit

The Fruit of the Spirit are evidence of Holy Spirit living inside of you and of your new life in Christ. As you are growing closer to God, allowing Him to be Lord of your life, and continuing to strengthen your spirit, you will see more evidence of the Fruit of the Spirit in you. The Fruit of the Spirit aren't necessarily *tools* to use to strengthen our spirit like the other three I mentioned, but they are a way for us to see how well we're doing in allowing our spirit to lead instead of our soul or body.

> *But the fruit of the Spirit is love, joy, peace, long-suffering, kindness, goodness, faithfulness, gentleness, self-control. Against such there is no law. Galatians 5:22-23*

Go back to chapter 3 and look back over the list of reasons that you wrote down that people may overeat. Look back at the ones that I mentioned as well. Many of the reasons we overeat are because the Fruit of the Spirit need to be matured more in that area.

For instance, if we're overeating because of stress, then we may be lacking peace and need to develop that Fruit more. If we're overeating because of sadness, then we need more joy. If we're not being disciplined, then we need more self-control. A lot of our struggle with overeating can be helped by developing the Fruit of the Spirit. We do that through our relationship with God, as we're walking in His ways, and allowing Him to be Lord over our lives. Look at this list of the Fruit of the Spirit below. Circle which ones you believe may be underdeveloped in your life. Which ones really stand out for you that you would like to mature and display more of in your life?

- Love

- Joy

- Peace

- Longsuffering (Patience)

- Kindness

- Goodness

- Faithfulness

- Gentleness

- Self-Control

Of the ones that you circled, pick one to start with. Pray and ask God to help you in that area. Read scriptures or stories that focus on that Fruit. Take notice of it when you see it being displayed in the Bible. If you're not sure where to find verses or stories, you can start with a quick search on the internet for it. Also start looking for ways and situations that come up in your own life where you can practice displaying that Fruit more. If you have a prayer journal, then document your progress as you strengthen your spirit. It'll be a great testimony in the future that you can share with someone else who is struggling in the same area that you once were.

> *For a good tree does not bear bad fruit, nor does a bad tree bear good fruit. For every tree is known by its own fruit. For men do not gather figs from thorns, nor do they gather grapes from a bramble bush. A good man out of the good treasure of his heart brings forth good; and an evil man out of the evil treasure of his heart brings forth evil. For out of the abundance of the heart his mouth speaks. Luke 6:43-45*

Like I mentioned before, there are more than 4 tools that we have as a believer, but these are ones that you can easily start with on your own. Others that you may want to utilize and should at some point may include learning to put on the whole armor of God (Ephesians 6:10-20), asking for prayer and prophetic intercessory, getting inner healing and deliverance, and even praying in the Spirit. Start with these four tools for now to take your spirit to the gym so that you can strengthen your spirit and your ears will be more in tune to Holy Spirit. He can and He will lead and guide you instead of those sugar cravings if you let Him.

Now that we have a workout plan for your spirit. Let's look at what we can do for our soul next.

Chapter 6

TAKING CARE OF YOUR SOUL

How many times have we been led to overeat because of negative thoughts, because we *just wanted to*, or because we were emotional. Our soul is not a great leader and this just reminds us of how important it is for us to be spirit-led instead. Our soul is our mind, will, and emotions and following it will usually lead to destruction or in our case falling back into the sin of gluttony. Let's take a look at two tools to help us take more control of our soul.

We're going to focus mostly on our mind and thoughts because those can have a big impact on our will and emotions. Have you tried to use willpower before to stop overeating but couldn't? At least not long term. I believe...

the real willpower comes in submitting to His will for our lives.

I also believe that it's hard to will yourself to stop overeating when you haven't worked on changing some of the thoughts or deep beliefs that you have around food and sweets. Maybe your issue isn't lack of willpower, but it's that you overeat at times when you're highly emotional. Well your emotions are often a direct reflection of the thoughts that you're thinking at that moment. So we need to learn how to take those thoughts captive and establish beliefs centered around God's truth. That way we're no longer turning to sweets or food instead of our Lord and Savior.

Normally when most of us feel ready to lose weight, we jump straight into action and try to change those unhealthy habits that we're doing. It seems like the logical thing to do, but that isn't what we should start with. When you look at the Transtheoretical Model[2], also called Stages of Change Model, you see that Action is step number 4. The previous three steps are Precontemplation, Contemplation, and Preparation. For now, don't worry about what each one actually means. The point is that the 3 steps that need to occur before any lasting behavior change can happen are all related to your thoughts and beliefs. Once the thoughts and beliefs are changed, *then* you move into action and can have lasting results.

Our thoughts and beliefs influence our actions, and those actions that we take produce a certain result. If we want to change the results that we're getting, we have to change the actions we're taking. If I want to stop gaining weight (result), then I have to stop overeating (action). Well, duh. You know this already. That's what makes us launch into action on January 1st. But because most of us jump straight to step 4 of the model without working on steps 1-3 first, we end up falling right back into our old behaviors. The key is in learning how to change those first three steps (thoughts and beliefs) so that the actions we're taking will actually be changed long term and we'll get new results. So how do we change our thoughts and beliefs?

Our beliefs are influenced by our thoughts and emotions. Our beliefs are certainly also influenced by our environment and by the way we grew up. But even those beliefs were formed by the thoughts that you had about what you heard or what you learned over time. Most of the actions that we are currently taking are based on these thoughts and beliefs. The crazy thing is that most of it is done on autopilot and we don't even realize that it is happening.

Eighty to ninety percent of what you do comes from the subconscious thoughts you have and what you are believing deep down. Unfortunately, those thoughts and beliefs aren't always good ones that serve you well. If we keep ending up with the same undesirable results or outcomes, then we need to back it up and look at our thoughts and beliefs about that thing.

Take a look at this analogy. Recently, I went on a road trip and had to rent a car for the trip. It was a much newer car than the one I'm currently driving. It had all the bells, whistles, and upgrades. Since it was a long trip, I decided once we were coasting to turn on the cruise control. I love being able to utilize cruise control because it gives me a chance to stretch my legs and give my big toe a break. The cruise control worked similar to what I was used to in my car. You set the speed and it maintains that speed until you tap the brake to slow it down or hit the gas to speed up. But once you take your foot off, it will automatically readjust and take you back to the speed that you set. Well that's how our subconscious thoughts and beliefs work with our weight loss attempts. We don't realize that our weight loss cruise control is set based on our mindset. We can speed things up on January 1st when we jump into action. But as soon as we take our foot off the gas or lose our motivation, it won't be long before we're coasting back at the speed we once were (back to the old actions).

This car was so cool that it even had one cruise control feature that my older car doesn't have. Whenever another car would come into my lane in front of me, the speed of the car would automatically adjust so that the cars wouldn't collide. Again it's similar in our weight loss journeys. Whenever we face obstacles or challenges in our path, our efforts to move forward can be slowed down without us actually putting our foot on the brake. The good news though is that we can change the settings on our weight loss cruise control.

We can change our thoughts and beliefs into ones that serve us better. We can change our mindset to one that the healthier version of ourselves would have. One where we can enjoy sweets without making them an idol. There are two methods that you can use together to change the end result you're getting and the original thoughts you're having that are leading to that result. Before we discuss those, let's look at how having a vision for your life can help you in this process.

Vision for Your Life

Remember that road trip I said I went on? By knowing where I wanted to go, I knew what route to take to get there. Having a vision for your life helps you to have a picture of where you want to end up. If you know where you want to end up, then that helps you to know what direction or actions you need to take to get there.

If you don't know your purpose or calling, then I want to encourage you to seek the Lord about it. Spend time in prayer and ask Him to reveal to you what His vision for your life is and what He has called you to do. Knowing this will help you to know what path to take so you can move forward toward His will for you.

> *Trust in the Lord with all your heart,*
> *And lean not on your own understanding;*
> *In all your ways acknowledge Him,*
> *And He shall direct your paths. Proverbs 3:5-6*

By knowing my destination on that road trip, I knew what route to take. But I also knew which one not to take. Having a vision for your life helps you to set boundaries and to know what you don't want to do. You'll be able to recognize more easily the thoughts, beliefs, and actions that aren't leading you toward your destination. Having this vision of the purpose-filled, healthier version of you will help when we look at the two tools for our soul. It'll be easier for you to start changing your thoughts, beliefs, and actions to line up with the path you want to take.

Take a moment now and seek God for the vision for your life. Write it in your prayer journal or jot down below what first comes to mind. Continue to seek Him to further develop this vision and give you more details and direction.

_____

_____

_____

_____

_____

The 4 S's - Saying, Settling, Stepping, Seeing

When you keep getting the same result over and over again and it's not the outcome you want, there are 4 things that you should observe. And because I love alliteration, I have made them all S words for you. We're going to look at what you're Saying, Settling, Stepping, and Seeing.

1. What are you **saying** to yourself? These are the thoughts in your head or the words that you may be saying out loud.

2. What's **settling** in your heart? This is what you're believing based on what you're saying to yourself.

3. How are you **stepping** into action? This is the action you are taking based on what you are believing and thinking.

4. What are you **seeing** as a result of this? These are the results or outcomes that you are getting based on the actions you are taking.

Let's work this out with an example and a fictional character.

Typically after a difficult day at work Sharon likes to eat a pint of ice cream to wind down. However, she wants to lose weight and this isn't helping her. She wants to stop doing it, but she keeps finding herself turning to the ice cream most weeks. Let's go through the 4 S's with Sharon.

Saying: What is she saying to herself?
"It's been a long day. I'm tired. I'm stressed. I just want to relax and chill. I don't really want to have to think about anything difficult for the next few hours. I don't even feel like cooking"

Settling: What's settling in her heart?
"I deserve a reward after the day I had. I should treat myself."

Stepping: How is she stepping into action?
She grabs her favorite pint of ice cream and finds a romantic comedy movie to watch so she can unwind.

Seeing: What is she seeing as a result?
She ends up feeling worse because now she has blown her eating plan for the week. She starts feeling guilt and shame. Telling herself this is why she can't ever lose weight and then ends up eating even more. The scale is up the next morning.

This is obviously not the result that Sharon wants. So one way that she can change what she is *seeing* is by backing it up all the way to what she is *saying*. What you are saying to yourself matters. The thoughts you have matter. They affect what you believe which affects what you do which is what gets you the outcomes that you've been experiencing. Before we get into changing our thoughts and what we're saying to ourselves, let's look at how you can do this.

Here's the scenario. Someone brings a box of your favorite kind of donuts to work or to a meeting that you're attending, but you weren't planning on eating donuts that day.

Saying: What are you saying to yourself? These are the thoughts in your head or even the words you may be saying out loud.

_____

_____

_____

_____

_____

Settling: What's settling in your heart? This is what you're believing based on what you're saying to yourself.

_____

_____

_____

_____

_____

Stepping: How are you stepping into action? This is the action you are taking based on what you are believing and thinking.

_____

_____

_____

_____

_____

Seeing: What are you seeing as a result of this? These are the results or outcomes that you are getting based on the actions you are taking.

_____

_____

_____

_____

_____

You can use this tool to discover what thoughts you have on autopilot that are getting you the results that you keep seeing and want to change. What's great is that you can also use the 4 S's to get the result you *want* to get instead. All you have to do is work backwards. Here's how that looks.

What is the result you *want* to **see**?

What are the **steps** you need to take to see it?

What needs to **settle** in your heart (believe) to take those steps?

What do you need to **say** to yourself to settle that in your heart?

Try it now. Let's use the example of meal planning. Your goal is to start planning your meals for the week so you have more opportunities to eat healthier. (I should probably do this one too.)

What is the result you want to **see**?

_____

_____

_____

_____

_____

What are the **steps** you need to take to see it?

_____

_____

_____

_____

_____

What do you need to **settle** in your heart (believe) to take those steps?

_____

_____

_____

_____

_____

What do you need to **say** to yourself to settle that in your heart?

_____

_____

_____

_____

_____

We're talking specifically about using these 4 S's to help our soul in the area of overeating, but you can certainly use this process in any area of your life where you keep getting a result that you're not happy with. Try using it for those areas too. You can download some 4 S's worksheets at ChristOverCookies.com/extras.

Now we can see how our thoughts affect our actions and the results that we are ultimately getting. We know now what we want to think, but like I mentioned, the majority of our thoughts are subconscious ones and we're mostly operating on autopilot. So unless we know how to change our thoughts and reset our cruise control, we're probably going to default back to those thoughts that lead to the behaviors and outcomes that we don't want. So let's look at how we change those thoughts to new ones that serve us better.

R.E.N.E.W.ing Your Mind

We are going to R.E.N.E.W. our minds, change our thoughts, and reset that cruise control. This is the second tool for you to use for your soul.

> *And do not be conformed to this world, but be transformed by the renewing of your mind, that you may prove what is that good and acceptable and perfect will of God. Romans 12:2*

If you went through the previous questions with the 4 S's, then you see how much your thoughts matter and influence the behaviors and outcomes you're getting. So we need to work on making mindset shifts so that we have better thoughts to help us to have better actions and stop overeating.

We can do this through a journaling acronym that I call R.E.N.E.W. This is great to use as a proactive tool for those situations when you are tempted to overeat but haven't yet. It's also great as a reactive one when you have already overeaten and want to make a change for the next time.

R

The R in R.E.N.E.W. stands for **recognize the lie or rationalization**. What is the lie that the enemy is trying to tell you? Or how are you trying to rationalize overeating?

If we look back at the example with Sharon, we can recognize the lie or rationalization in what she was saying to herself and settling in her heart. She was telling herself that she had a difficult day, which may have been true. But she believed that she deserved a treat for it. Was that true? Do you deserve to treat yourself because you've had a bad day? She was trying to rationalize, or justify, why it was ok for her to have the treat. So step 1, the R, is to write down the lie that the enemy is trying to deceive you with or the rationalization that you may be telling yourself.

E

The first E in R.E.N.E.W. is for **erase it**. Whatever you've written down as the lie or rationalization, I want you to cross it off. It's not true. So I want you to physically see yourself scratching off that thought, putting a line through it, or scribbling it out. It's no longer true for you.

You may be tempted to do this exercise digitally, but I want to encourage you to actually do this with pen and paper. There's science behind the actual benefits to your brain of writing things down physically. But if you're not trying to hear me, then go ahead and type it out, then use the strikethrough feature to cross off the lie.

N

The N is for **new thought**. What is the new thought that you want to have? This is where you get to replace that lie with your new truth. This is where you get to start coming up with new thoughts to lead you to new beliefs and ultimately new results. These are the thoughts that you want to have that line up with the vision for your life. I'll walk you through a full example of this with Sharon in a moment.

E

The second E in R.E.N.E.W. stands for **echo it**. You know when you shout something and there's an echo, it's repeated. So you are literally going to repeat that new thought to yourself. I want you to repeat it 7 times after you write it, preferably out loud. Then each time the old lie tries to pop up in your head or you hear yourself saying it, then repeat the new thought again 7 times.

There's a saying I have that...

> the words you *say repeatedly*
> are the words you *hear constantly*
> and the words you *believe deeply*.

So echo it. I'm also going to give you a bonus hack for this that you can implement.

W

The last letter in R.E.N.E.W., W, stands for the **Word of God**. What does the Word of God say to back up your new thought? This is where you get to confirm your new thought with God's truth. As believers this helps us to align what we're thinking and believing with the truth of God's Word. Look up verses that coincide with and confirm the new thought you want to establish. Pray and ask the Lord to lead you to scripture that He wants you to read about it. And bonus, if you memorize those verses as well.

We demolish arguments and every pretension that sets itself up against the knowledge of God, and we take captive every thought to make it obedient to Christ. 2 Corinthians 10:5 NIV

This last step helps us to take those negative thoughts and lies captive.

Let's walk through R.E.N.E.W. with the example we had before with Sharon and the pint of ice cream after the difficult day at work. Here's what it would look like for her.

Recognize the lie or rationalization:
I had a difficult day at work. I deserve a treat

Erase it:
~~I had a difficult day at work. I deserve a treat~~

New thought:
I had a difficult day at work and praise music always helps me de-stress and puts me in a better mood.

Echo it:
Sharon repeats the new thought 7 times.

Word of God:
The Lord is my strength and my shield; My heart trusted in Him, and I am helped; Therefore my heart greatly rejoices, And with my song I will praise Him. Psalm 28:7

Be anxious for nothing, but in everything by prayer and supplication, with thanksgiving, let your requests be made known to God; and the peace of God, which surpasses all understanding, will guard your hearts and minds through Christ Jesus. Philippians 4:6-7

So that's an example of how that would look for Sharon and how she could begin to change her thoughts so that she can change her results. You can see how if she now has this thought and turns to praise music instead of the pint then that will still support her health goals that she has for herself. And bonus, she will be growing closer to the Lord as she is praising Him.

Now try it for yourself. Think of a thought that you have repeatedly that is leading you down a negative spiral and to results that you don't want. If you can't think of the thought, go through the previous 4 S's process backwards from the result you keep getting. That way you can figure out what the thought is that you need to replace.

Recognize the lie or rationalization. Write it down below.

_____

_____

_____

_____

_____

Erase it. Go back up and put a line through or scribble through that lie.

New thought. Write the new thought that you want to have instead.

_____

_____

_____

_____

_____

Echo it. Repeat that new thought out loud right now 7 times. And <u>every time</u> the enemy tries to whisper that old lie or the rationalization tries to pop up in your mind, then say that new thought out loud again 7 times.

Word of God. Find verses that confirm that new thought and write them below.

_____

_____

_____

_____

_____

Use this exercise every time you recognize a new lie or rationalization that comes up for you. I put an additional blank R.E.N.E.W. worksheet on ChristOverCookies.com/extras that you can print off as well.

Let me give you a way to hack this R.E.N.E.W. process that I learned from Heather Shriver Burns[3], my Kingdom Neuroscience Coach. Yes, that's a real thing. One of the ways that I mentioned to get this new thought into your subconscious is to E, echo it. To make the echoing process easier, when you write out your new thought, record it. Record yourself saying all of the new thoughts that you are making your new truths. Then, listen to them daily. Listen to them first thing in the morning and last thing in the evening. Heather suggests doing this consecutively for about 67 days.

Around day 21, she says your brain is going to throw a toddler tantrum. You're going to want to quit doing it and your brain is going to argue with you and tell you that this new thought isn't true. Press through the urge to stop and continue listening. Hearing these new thoughts repeatedly for 67 days will help to get them into your subconscious mind. And that helps you to reset that cruise control. If you're a rockstar, and I know you are, then do it for 90 days instead of 67. I put a habit tracker on that website I just mentioned so you can check it off each day as you listen to it in the morning and evening.

Now you have a vision for your life and two powerful tools in your box to help you with the soul - your mind, will, and emotions. Let's move on to the third side of us.

Chapter 7

SUBDUING YOUR BODY

As I mentioned, we tend to allow our body and soul or our flesh to lead us instead of the spirit. But now we know that's out of order and that we are to be spirit-led. There will be times though during your journey to end gluttony that your flesh is going to cry out and try to take the lead again. These 2 verses can help to serve as a reminder during those times that our bodies want to do what our bodies want to do.

Or do you not know that your body is the temple of the Holy Spirit who is in you, whom you have from God, and you are not your own? For you were bought at a price; therefore glorify God in your body and in your spirit, which are God's. 1 Corinthians 6:19-20

This is a great reminder that Jesus Christ died on the cross for us and that we are not our own. That means that what we do with our bodies should be glorifying and honoring Him because they are His.

> *I beseech you therefore, brethren, by the mercies of God, that you present your bodies a living sacrifice, holy, acceptable to God, which is your reasonable service. Romans 12:1*

If we're presenting our bodies as a living sacrifice, then we're not giving in to everything that the body wants to do. If we are making a sacrifice, we are instead doing what God wants us to do with our bodies.

Let's take a look at a few practical tools that we can use to help us stop overeating sweets, keep our bodies in check, and honor God with what we're doing with them.

Change Your Environment

One of the simplest things we can do in this area to help us to stop overeating is change our environment. Doing this alone won't help you stop completely. But what it does is makes it harder for you to overeat and easier for you to succeed.

Let's say that you have a problem with overeating cookies. You always intend to eat just one or two, but before you know it you've eaten a whole sleeve of cookies. So change your environment by no longer bringing the cookies in the house. If you know that you are more likely to fall into gluttony if you have them in the house, then don't bring them in there in the first place.

That way when you have a craving for the cookies you have one of 2 options. One, you can find something else to satisfy that craving in the moment like a sweet piece of fruit. Or two, you can go to the store each time you have the craving to get the cookies. Option one helps you to make healthier choices. Option 2 gives you multiple opportunities to realize you don't actually need the cookies and decide not to go get them. Every step of the way to the store, Holy Spirit can chime in and remind you that you don't actually need the cookies and that there are other options. By the way, I'm not saying don't ever have the cookies. But if you know you lack self control with them, then changing your environment can help you reduce the number of times you actually overeat.

Another way you can change your environment is by having healthier options that you are more likely to have control with when you are craving something sweet. Sort of like I mentioned with option one above. For example, I used to eat a slice of cake pretty much everyday. One thing I decided to do in the beginning of my weight loss journey was find other sweets that I could have that weren't as many calories but that would still satisfy the craving. So I would have those in the house instead. That worked for a while to help me have my sweets and still lose weight too. I did that until I got to a point where I was ready to yield my sweet tooth over to the Lord.

If you have a situation where you can't control if those cookies are in the house or not, then my suggestion is putting your Bible in the cabinet on top of them. Or at least a sticky note on the package if you don't want people questioning why your Bible is in the pantry. This is going to serve as a reminder for you to choose *Christ Over Cookies*. It's going to be a way for you to pause and ask yourself why you're having the cookies in the first place. If you just want it, then have it. But if you're turning to them at a time when you should be turning to the Lord then pick up that Bible instead.

Organizing your kitchen is another great way to change up your environment. Decluttering your kitchen actually has a positive effect on your mindset. Plus it helps to make meal time less frustrating because everything is organized and in place.

While you're reorganizing your kitchen, consider getting smaller plates. Using smaller plates could help you unintentionally eat less. My kids love to eat chicken nuggets and little pizza rolls. One of my sons will grab a plate and put as many as he can on that plate. He fills it. This kid is growing and is full of energy so I understand it's normal for boys his age to try to eat everything in sight. Nevertheless, without fail he fills up the plate with the chicken nuggets or the pizza rolls. If I buy smaller plates, by default he's going to eat less because he won't be able to fit as many on his plate. The same will work for us adults. There have been studies that have shown that we tend to eat whatever is served to us. So if we are given smaller plates, we will be more likely to eat less. This especially helps if you're a member of the clean plate club and feel guilty about not eating everything on your plate and throwing food away. But we'll talk about that in a minute. In the meantime, grab some smaller sized plates and make sure they're pretty because that makes a difference too.

Change Your Routine

Changing your routine is another way that you can change your environment. Are you stopping at the coffee shop every day out of habit? Or maybe you're swinging into the drive through on the way home. Try going a different route. Those places may be acting as triggers for you and your autopilot response is to pull into them. If you go a different route, that changes up those patterns. You may find a new healthy restaurant on the way home to try instead. Or you can make coffee at home, that'll probably be lower calorie and lower cost, and drive a new way to work so you don't go by that old coffee shop.

One of the things that has really helped me this time in my weight loss journey is establishing a morning routine. It sets the tone of the day for me and also there are triggers in my morning routine that just help to remind me that I'm on my weight loss journey and keeps me mindful. Almost every morning looks pretty much the same for me. I wake up, go to the bathroom, then take the dog out. That's not the important part of the routine, but I think my dog would disagree with me on that. After that I get on the scale and get dressed for the day. I have my morning time with the Lord. Plan out meals for the day. Fill up my water bottle and get the rest of the day started.

There are key things in my routine that keep me on track and mindful of my mission to continue to choose *Christ Over Cookies*. First I weigh myself daily. This is not something I suggest that everyone does. Especially if you tend to make your weight an idol or if the number on the scale will have an affect on your emotions or mentality for the day. I just do it as a tool to remind me of what I'm doing and a checkpoint because I love numbers and seeing how my weight fluctuates each day. Spending time with the Lord before I spend time with anyone else also sets the tone for my day. I'm able to spend time in peace and in conversation with the love of my life (God). Spending time with Him first also helps me to keep my priorities straight. After that I plan out my meals for the day. I'm pretty mood driven about what I eat and I tend to eat what I feel like I want that day. This can easily lead to overeating and falling into gluttony. So I plan out my meals for the day right after I spend time with the Lord. That way I still get to eat what I want that day, but it's within reason so I have less chance of overeating. After I've planned my meals, I get up and fill up my water bottle. Drinking water was a struggle for me at the beginning of my weight loss journey. In fact, I drank no water before. So I have to be intentional about making sure I do it daily. So filling up a half gallon water bottle and having it stare it at me on my desk all day reminds me to drink it.

Your routine doesn't have to be complicated or with as much detail. It could be just one simple thing. In fact, I would suggest that you start simple. One of my coaching clients puts her workout clothes in the bathroom before she goes to bed. That way when she wakes up in the morning and goes to the bathroom the clothes are sitting there as a reminder and trigger to put them on and get ready to exercise. Just change up your routine and establish something that is going to serve as a reminder for you of the journey you are on.

Build Healthy Habits

Another tool that helps with your flesh is building healthy habits. When health becomes a habit, it's just something you do automatically. It's a part of your weight loss cruise control. And don't worry about trying to change everything all at once. Pick one positive habit that will serve you and honor God to start with. Once that habit is established, you'll see that it has a ripple effect and you'll naturally want to do more positive things for your body.

A few years ago, I started going to a dance fitness class first thing in the mornings, three times a week. I'm not a huge fan of exercise. That's a thought that I need to take through the 4 S's and the R.E.N.E.W process. I love dancing so this was a way for me to move my body more and have fun while doing it. I noticed that as I started going to the exercise classes regularly on those days I would also eat better. I didn't want to eat junk food after exercise class and would end up eating healthier options on the days that I went to class. I felt so good that I wanted to do something more positive for myself after. It was like a ripple effect.

One of the other things I realized is that the more healthy stuff I had coming in took up space so there wasn't as much room for the unhealthy options. In the beginning of my weight loss journey, I was drinking about 2 liters of soda a day. I knew this was one of the first habits I wanted to change. I would drink all soda and no water whatsoever. We need on average about 3 liters of water a day. One liter of that is going to come from our food so the other 2 liters or so we should be drinking. I was drinking none. So I started working on that habit first. And now I rarely drink anything else except for water. Making the commitment to myself to drink 2 liters of water a day doesn't leave much room for me to drink anything else because I pretty much need to drink water at each meal. It helps to fill me up and it has so many other benefits for my body too.

Besides working on moving your body more or drinking more water, you could also start to work on improving your sleep. You want to make sure you are getting an adequate amount of quality sleep. Your sleeping habits affect your level of stress and believe it or not impacts how you eat. If you're waking up tired and cranky, think of ways that you can either get more hours of sleep or a better quality of sleep.

Eat More Mindfully

Being mindful of what you are eating and why is another great habit to establish. Take a moment to pause and ask yourself why you are eating or getting ready to eat something. Let's take the example of cookies from before. If you find yourself grabbing some cookies, ask yourself why are you reaching for the cookies right now. This is where having the Bible in the cabinet helps because it acts as a trigger to take a moment to pause.

No temptation has overtaken you except such as is common to man; but God is faithful, who will not allow you to be tempted beyond what you are able, but with the temptation will also make the way of escape, that you may be able to bear it. 1 Corinthians 10:13-14

If you want the cookies because it's just a craving you're having and you know you can have just one or two, then eat the cookies. Or you may want to ask yourself what else you can have to satisfy that craving that may be a healthier option for you, like perhaps fruit or yogurt. If you realize that you are reaching for the cookies because you're stressed or emotional, then that's a good time to stop and seek the Lord. After you've done that you could also go through the 4 S's or the R.E.N.E.W. exercise if you realize this is a pattern that you want to change.

Another way to be more mindful with your eating is focusing on the *way* you're actually eating. Studies have shown that we tend to eat more when we are distracted. So get rid of the distractions during mealtimes. Be more intentional about eating in a peaceful environment without the phone, television, or computer. If you're eating with others, then focus on having conversations with them instead of electronics. You also may want to try to slow down your eating. After each bite try putting your fork down, chewing and swallowing your food, then taking a sip of water if you'd like also. As you slow down the pace of your eating and are removing the distractions, you're giving your brain a chance to recognize the cues from your body that you are full. That helps you to eat less and avoid overeating and overstuffing yourself.

Quit the Clean Plate Club

In America, many kids grow up hearing that they need to clean their plates and not waste any food. It was a privilege to have an abundance of food and some kids weren't as fortunate. So if it's on your plate, then you eat it. As a mom, I certainly get how children can be wasteful when it comes to food and toilet paper for that matter. Like I mentioned before, my son would fill up his plate regardless of the size. But what can happen as we become adults is that we have this habit of cleaning our plates and eating everything on them, even when we're full. We can't seem to throw it away, because then it would be wasting it. But is it? I learned quickly in coaching that many of my clients had the same issue. Their moms were probably telling them a similar thing growing up. They were being told that if they were throwing away food then they were wasting it. My response to that is...

we're either going to waste it or waist it.

As we are working to glorify God with our bodies, know that treating our bodies as the garbage can isn't how to do it. Learn to quit the clean plate club. If you are full, it's ok to stop eating and leave food on your plate. If it's enough, then save it for later or for a meal the next day. If it's not and you're done eating for the day, then throw it away. I promise I won't tell your mother.

Fast

Therefore, dear brothers and sisters, you have no obligation to do what your sinful nature urges you to do. For if you live by its dictates, you will die. But if through the power of the Spirit you put to death the deeds of your sinful nature, you will live. Romans 8:12-13 NLT

Spiritual fasting is another tool that you can use for your body. Like I mentioned when we discussed this as a tool for your spirit, when you fast it helps to kill the desires of your flesh. That's why it's also a good tool for our body in this fight to stop the sin of gluttony and continue to choose *Christ Over Cookies*. Let's say that you decide to give up sweets for 40 days. When you go on your fast, your body, your flesh is going to cry out for those sweets. During the times that you would normally eat sweets, you want to make sure you are spending time with the Lord, praying, and reading His word. For instance, if I was fasting from that nightly piece of cake I used to have, then I would instead read my Bible during that time and enjoy some spiritual food. Spiritual fasting is such a good way to deny our flesh and make it submit to the spirit.

At one point in my journey, I made a decision to fast from sweets the first week of every month. That one thing was probably the most important for me to remove my sweet tooth. I noticed that because of fasting from sweets during that week, I actually wanted sweets less the rest of the time. The first month that I decided to not have sweets for the first seven days I actually ended up not having them for almost the entire month. And it wasn't on purpose. Maybe it was because I broke the habit of having them so frequently. Or maybe the craving was just gone. But for whatever reason, I was at the end of the month and realized that I still hadn't had anything sweet even though I had told myself that I could have it starting on day 8. Now, I don't eat sweets nearly as often. There's some months that I don't have them at all. I just don't *need* them anymore.

If you're overeating sweets like I was, and I'm guessing you may be since you're reading this book, then I want to suggest starting with this tool for your body. Like I said it had the most significant impact on me to help me stop craving sweets so much. You don't have to cut it out for 7 full days every month. I didn't do that when I first got started. What if you decide to not have sweets the first 3 days of every month? Or maybe even just the first day of each month? Start somewhere. Remember that during the time that you would normally eat something sweet or when you are craving something sweet during your fast then go to the Lord and ask Him for strength.

Side note: If you cut out the sugar for multiple days, you may find that you have headaches, you're cranky, or your energy is low because you're not on the sugar high. Push through, make your flesh submit, and seek the Lord. We have to wonder how good this stuff is for our bodies if it is reacting this way when we don't have it for short periods of time.

Have Accountability

Beware, brethren, lest there be in any of you an evil heart of unbelief in departing from the living God; but exhort one another daily, while it

is called "Today," lest any of you be hardened
through the deceitfulness of sin. Hebrews 3:12-13

Just like it's important to fellowship with like-minded believers in our walk with Christ to help us to persevere, it's important to have accountability as you work on becoming healthier. Having someone or a group of someones that you can call for support, encouragement, or accountability is key. One of the most important things I do for my coaching clients is hold them accountable. Having someone to "report to" makes you think twice about some of the actions you take. Holy Spirit will first and foremost be your accountability partner and trust me He will hold you accountable. I've heard His voice in my head many times telling me why I don't need to have another cupcake. Honestly, sometimes I listen and sometimes I don't. I repent and work on being a better listener the next time. Some of us, though, do well with having someone checking in on us regularly as well.

Get coaching, join challenge groups, or find a friend that will hold you accountable. Make sure it's someone that is strong enough to hold you accountable, but that also will not condemn you when you fall. You want someone that can pray for you when you regress and that'll give you a high five when you make progress. The Lord knows that we need each other and that there's power in numbers. When you get personal training, they try to get you to have a friend join you or to do group training. They know that you are more likely to commit and show up if you know there is a friend or group of friends waiting for you to come to the gym. If there's no one waiting and you don't feel like going, you probably just won't go that day. After a few times, you'll probably quit going altogether. It's the same for our weight loss journeys. We are more likely to stick to it when we have accountability.

Pick one of these tools for your body to start with. Remember don't get overwhelmed by it all. You can always come back to the other ones later. Pick one for now. Implement and master it. Then come back to work on the next thing.

Chapter 8

WHAT DO I DO NEXT?

Now you are armed with multiple tools, Biblical and practical. You know how to take your spirit to the gym to strengthen it. You can reset the cruise control that your soul is set to. And you know how to subdue your body and start creating habits that will serve you better on your health journey. All of these tools for your spirit, soul, and body will help you in overcoming the sin of gluttony.

I want to encourage you that you can do this. In our weakness, He is made strong. Allow the Lord to do a work in you so that you can put the sin of gluttony behind you and walk in freedom. Life is so much better when you aren't weighed down, literally and figuratively. Not to mention how good it feels when you conquer overeating and are no longer in bondage to the desires of your flesh.

Remember not to try to implement all of these tools at once. Pray and ask the Lord which one you should start with. Again I recommend starting with the tools for the spirit so you can focus on being more spirit-led instead of led by the flesh. I also recommend finding some account-ability sooner rather than later. I would love to see this message of freedom from the sin of gluttony being teached from more pulpits across the nations. It would be awesome to see church focus groups popping up as a result of it to support those that want to be free.

I'm not going to tell you that this journey will be easy. You have to be intentional about living a healthy life just as you do with most things that are good to have. We can't just drift into them. Good grades, a good marriage, a healthy body, none of those things happen by accident. You have to be intentional about doing the tasks necessary to keep moving toward them. Drifting only takes you towards what you don't want.

Your soul and your body are going to keep trying to lead. You'll be tempted at times to overeat and submit to the desires of your flesh or to grab some ice cream when you're feeling emotional. But now you know ways to put your mind, will, emotions, and flesh in check and allow your spirit to lead. If you do find yourself falling into gluttony, remember to give yourself some grace. It happens to all of us with this struggle. Our God is full of grace and mercy. Repent and ask Him to help you do better next time.

I want to encourage you to go through the *40 Days of Choosing Christ Over Cookies Devotional* in the next chapter. Give up sweets, or whatever your food is that you tend to overeat, for 40 days. Read the devotional first thing in the morning each day or during that time that you would normally eat whatever it is that you're giving up. This is a great way to get into the practice of praying, reading your Bible, and fasting - 3 of the 4 spiritual tools we discussed. And you don't have to do it alone. Get some accountability and go through the 40 days with someone or do it with a group.

Let's pray!

Lord, I appreciate each and every woman (and man) that is reading this book. You know her heart and that she picked up this book because she loves You and wants to give You glory with how she is living her life. Lord, I pray that she grows closer to You and that with the power of God that is within her, that she uses these principles and tools to break free of the stronghold that sweets and food has on her life. Lord, give her strength when she may feel weak. Remind her to continue to choose You and turn to You instead of food. Thank You Lord that by overcoming the sin of gluttony, she is showing others that through You they can do it too and that gives You all the glory. Thank You for Your grace, Your mercy, and Your unfailing love for us. We love You. In Jesus' Name, Amen.

Chapter 9

40 DAYS OF CHOOSING CHRIST OVER COOKIES

A Devotional

This isn't your ordinary devotional that you open up and read for five minutes in the morning so you can check off time spent with the Lord. This is warfare. This is your battle plan to take back control over that thing that has had control over you.

For the next 40 days, give up sweets, or whatever *your* thing is, and go through this devotional. If you're not sure what to give up, then seek the Lord and ask Him to show you. If your first thought is that you don't want to give it up for that long, then that's probably evidence that you should. Remember nothing, especially no food, should have that much power over you.

If you give in to the temptation and have it or you have it because you forgot you were fasting (ask me how I know that one), give yourself some grace. Ask for forgiveness and get right back to your fast. Don't let it turn into one of those *oh, I messed up so I might as well start again tomorrow* scenarios. Jump back in immediately.

Pray before you start this 40 day partial fast and ask the Lord to give you strength. Keep in mind any medical advice that you need to adhere to. Make sure to take notes in your prayer journal about what the Lord is showing you and speaking to you each day. Also take notes on what is happening with your flesh. You're going to uncover a lot about yourself and your relationship with food over these 40 days. If you can, do this with a friend or a group of friends. It helps to have others to pray for you, support you, and encourage you during this time.

In the space below, write what you are giving up for the next 40 days.

For the next 40 days, I am choosing Christ over

_____

_____

Day 1

Present Your Bodies

I beseech you therefore, brethren, by the mercies of God, that you present your bodies a living sacrifice, holy, acceptable to God, which is your reasonable service. Romans 12:1

When Apostle Paul is using the term beseech here, he is saying it to mean that he is urging you or appealing to you. In the words of Paul, I am saying it to you now that I beseech you sisters to present your bodies a living sacrifice.

When I think of the word present, I think of presenting someone with a gift. I wouldn't present them with just anything. I want to give them a good gift that they are excited to have. That's how it is when you present your body as a living sacrifice to God. You're giving Him one of the best gifts that you can give. You. Your obedience.

You are a living sacrifice because daily you are willing to submit to His will for you and His ways instead of the desires of your flesh. As Apostle Paul says, that's your reasonable service. That's the least that you and I can do considering what the Lord has done for us.

As you continue on this 40 day journey of choosing *Christ Over Cookies*, remember this verse. Each day wake up and make the commitment to present your body a living sacrifice.

Prayer

Father, I come to You as a willing, living sacrifice. Help me to remember the sacrifice that was made for me and that this is my reasonable service. Show me how to live and eat in a way that is acceptable to You and that honors You. Thank You Lord for seeing my body, as it is right now, as a good gift that I get to present to You. In Jesus' Name, Amen.

Day 2

Renew Your Mind

And do not be conformed to this world, but be transformed by the renewing of your mind, that you may prove what is that good and acceptable and perfect will of God. Romans 12:2

We are constantly being bombarded by what the world says about us, our lives, our families, and how we should look, act, and think. As someone who is trying to be in this world but not of it, it can be a challenge when the world's message is in your face daily through social media, the news, television programming, and movies. Some of those messages are bound to leak in though. That's why, as believers, we have to constantly renew our minds.

When we hear anything that comes from any place other than the Word of God, we have to test it against the Word. It doesn't matter if it's coming from the internet or from the mouths of our best friends. We have to see if it's in alignment with what God says about us, our lives, our families, and how we should look, act, and think. If it doesn't line up, then do not be conformed to it. Do not allow that to be your truth and keep on renewing your mind.

Prayer

Father, thank You that You have given me Your Word so that I can renew my mind daily when I read it. Help me to have the strength to be transformed by You and not conformed to the world. Lord, as I'm faced with the messages, images, and temptations of the world, show me what is Your good, acceptable, and perfect will for me. In Jesus' Name, Amen.

Day 3

It Is Well

"Please run now to meet her, and say to her, 'Is it well with you? Is it well with your husband? Is it well with the child?'" And she answered, "It is well."
2 Kings 4:26

There will be times during this 40 day partial fast when you won't feel great, because you're not having your favorite treat. There may be headaches, crankiness, sluggishness, and probably even more temptations than usual because the enemy just doesn't play fair. I want to encourage you to declare through it all that *it is well*.

In this story the woman's young son had passed. This son was her promised child that she had been given because of her service and faithfulness to God. When he died, she immediately left the house and went straight to Elisha the prophet who had spoken the promise over her. When he asked her if everything was ok, she declared *it is well*. You know what? It was. Elisha took the matter to the Lord and her son was resurrected.

I believe that she was speaking by faith and not by sight. She was declaring what she knew in the spiritual, not what was happening in the natural. I want to encourage you to do the same when those sugar withdrawal symptoms start coming up. They are happening *to* you physically, but there's something much greater happening *in* you spiritually. After a few days, those symptoms are going to go away, the fog will clear, and you will see that *it is well*.

Prayer

Father, thank You that because of the good work You are doing in me, I can declare that it is well. Give me strength to continue on this journey with You when the sugar withdrawals and cravings hit. Remind me that I'm learning to crave You instead of them. In Jesus' Name, Amen.

Day 4

Letting It Go

Jesus said to him, "If you want to be perfect, go, sell what you have and give to the poor, and you will have treasure in heaven; and come, follow Me." But when the young man heard that saying, he went away sorrowful, for he had great possessions. Matthew 19:21-22

I can picture this rich, young man in this passage coming to Jesus thinking he has acquired all the worldly things, so now he wants to follow Jesus. Jesus basically tells him to trade in those worldly treasures for heavenly ones first, then come and follow Him. The young man leaves sad.

Maybe he didn't want to give up the possessions because of the time it took for him to accumulate them. Maybe he didn't want to give them up because his identity was tied to them. Maybe knowing that he had great possessions made him feel comforted and secure. Whatever his reason, he couldn't see that the value in having heavenly treasures and following Christ was greater than the value of what he treasured on earth.

We are going to be faced with that same decision in our war to overcome overeating. We are going to have to make the decision to give up overeating the sweets and food that we treasure on earth for the sweeter treasures in heaven. Will we listen to Holy Spirit's nudge to put down that second cupcake? Are we willing to stop after the first serving because we're actually full? Will we choose to fuel our faith or feed our faces? The choice to follow Him is always ours to make.

Prayer

Father, help me to crave You and Your presence more than anything. Help me to see that time and life with You is more satisfying than any cheat day or treat could ever be. Lord, teach me to cling to You instead of what I may treasure on earth. In Jesus' Name, Amen.

Day 5

Focus on Abundance

Now the serpent was more cunning than any beast of the field which the Lord God had made. And he said to the woman, "Has God indeed said, 'You shall not eat of every tree of the garden'?" Genesis 3:1

The enemy has this sneaky way of getting us to focus on lack and what we can't have instead of God's abundance and all the things that we can have. We see him doing this very thing in the Garden with Eve. The Lord had told them they could eat freely of every tree except that one. Abundance. Satan, however, pointed out how they could *not* eat of every tree. Lack. He got Eve to focus on lack and to start craving what she couldn't have.

He uses this same trick with us in our weight loss journeys, and he'll especially do it during this fast. He'll keep reminding you of the one thing that you can't have instead of the thousands of other foods that you can. Don't fall for his schemes. Make a list of all the foods that you can have during this partial fast. When the enemy tries to tempt you with the one you can't, go back to your list and pick something else to have instead.

<u>Prayer</u>

Father, thank You for giving me food in abundance and a plethora of choices to choose from. Remind me that in You, I lack nothing. I thank You and I love You. In Jesus' Name, Amen.

Day 6

Fix Your Eyes

So when the woman saw that the tree was good for food, that it was pleasant to the eyes, and a tree desirable to make one wise, she took of its fruit and ate. She also gave to her husband with her, and he ate. Genesis 3:6

Yesterday we saw how the enemy will get us to focus on lack to lead us to sin. Today's verse is a continuation of that story. The key here is that he got her to *focus* on what she couldn't have. Once he did that, the temptation started.

She saw that she could eat it, it looked good to eat, and that it would make her wise, so she ate it. Her eyes had become fixed on the temptation, and she gave in to sin.

When the enemy tries to get you to *focus* on your favorite food, the same can happen to you. You start thinking of how good it tastes and smells. You may start thinking of the warm and fuzzy feelings you get when you eat it. Your mouth may even start watering. Hold on sister. The longer the enemy can get us to keep our attention on the "forbidden treat", the more likely we are to give in to the temptation. Fix your eyes, or mind in this case, on something else. Preferably Jesus.

<u>Prayer</u>

Father, thank You for providing me with good food to eat and enjoy. When I'm tempted to have that treat that I just don't need or that I want to overeat, help me to fix my eyes on You and call me closer. In Jesus' Name, Amen.

Day 7

I'm a Slave For You

And the children of Israel said to them, "Oh, that we had died by the hand of the Lord in the land of Egypt, when we sat by the pots of meat and when we ate bread to the full! For you have brought us out into this wilderness to kill this whole assembly with hunger." Exodus 16:3

What?! I couldn't believe what I was reading here. The children of Israel would have rather died as slaves with their bellies full of food, than die as free people who were hungry. This verse is so eye opening to me about the power that food can have over our lives if we allow it. They wanted to trade in their freedom, their lives, for a stuffed belly. It sounds ridiculous. Until I realized, I did it too.

For me, it was my body, my beauty, and my freedom that I was willing to trade in for food. I thought that by turning to food and ultimately gaining weight that I was freeing myself from the opinions of others. In reality, I was a slave to them. I was willing to continue to be a slave as long as I was continuing to overeat.

Sister, what freedoms have you been willing to give up in exchange for food? Take a moment to think on it and declare that today is the last day that you do.

Prayer

Father, thank You that I get to walk in freedom because of Your Son, Jesus Christ. Show me the ways in which I'm trading in that freedom for a full belly and give me the strength to stop doing it. In Jesus' Name, Amen.

Day 8

Things You Say When You're Hangry

And Esau said to Jacob, "Please feed me with that same red stew, for I am weary." Therefore his name was called Edom. But Jacob said, "Sell me your birthright as of this day." And Esau said, "Look, I am about to die; so what is this birthright to me?" Genesis 25:30-32

Have you ever been so hungry that you said or did something that you later regretted? I know I have. We can see that Esau did too as we read on.

And Jacob gave Esau bread and stew of lentils; then he ate and drank, arose, and went his way. Thus Esau despised his birthright. Genesis 35:34

Hopefully, those sugar withdrawal symptoms have subsided by now. If they haven't, let this be your reminder that they are temporary and will be gone soon. Be more aware of what you're saying and how you're acting now and in times when you may be hungry. Make sure that what you're doing and saying stays in alignment with what God wants. It's so easy to get distracted by the hunger that we forget about the promise and inheritance ahead. Don't pull an Esau (or a Jacob for that matter).

Prayer

Father, thank You that no amount of food can satisfy me like You can. In the moments when I am hungry and cranky, remind me whose daughter I am and to act accordingly. In Jesus' Name, Amen.

Day 9

Sowing With Our Forks

Do not be deceived, God is not mocked; for whatever a man sows, that he will also reap. For he who sows to his flesh will of the flesh reap corruption, but he who sows to the Spirit will of the Spirit reap everlasting life. Galatians 6:7-8

Have you heard the saying that you get what you give? This is kind of what this is saying. You can't expect to live to please your flesh and get the rewards of the Spirit. In the same way, living to please the Spirit, won't leave you reaping the consequences of the flesh.

This law of sowing and reaping can apply to our weight loss journeys and battle with overcoming gluttony as well. If we give in to the desires of the flesh by overeating then we will get the rewards of the flesh- temporary satisfaction, expanding waistlines, sluggishness. But, if we're obedient to the Spirit's prompting to stop when we're full, then we get to reap life, energy, and fullness from Him.

Look for instances throughout this week when you can sow to the Spirit instead of the flesh. Don't forget to write them down in your journal.

Prayer

Father, thank You for this law of sowing and reaping. Remind me that I should live to please the Spirit not my flesh, and then I will receive everlasting life and life more abundantly. In Jesus' Name, Amen.

Day 10

You Are Marvelous

I will praise You, for I am fearfully and wonderfully made; Marvelous are Your works, And that my soul knows very well. Psalm 139:14

David really knew how to praise the Lord. We see evidence of that in all of the Psalms that he has written. You may have also heard that David was a man after God's own heart. What I love about this Psalm in particular is that while he is recognizing how awesome God is, David is also seeing how amazing he is too. Not in a prideful way either. He is saying that he is marvelous because God's works are marvelous.

Sister, you are marvelous too. Walk in that amazingness starting today. As women, we tend to overlook the beauty of our bodies whatever shape or size they may be, especially when we are working towards losing weight and getting healthier. Beautiful sister, just like David, you are one of God's works too. You are marvelous. Learn to love and appreciate your current body and the beauty of it.

Prayer

Father, thank You that I am fearfully and wonderfully made. Help me to see how marvelous I am the way that I see it in Your other works. Show me the beauty in my current body as I am working on my healthier body. In Jesus' Name, Amen.

Day 11

It's Your Move

"By your sword you shall live,
And you shall serve your brother;
And it shall come to pass, when you become restless,
That you shall break his yoke from your neck. "
Genesis 27:40

This was a part of the blessing that Isaac spoke over Esau before passing away. It has nothing to do with food, but he says something that caught my attention and can be important for us on our weight loss journeys. He told him that he would be serving his brother, but the power to be free from it was in his hands. Read the verse again.

We may feel powerless when it comes to the hold that food has over us. We've tried and tried again to stop overeating it, only to end up succumbing to it. At some point though, we finally get sick and tired of being sick and tired. We get tired of the extra weight and the weight of it. This verse should serve as a reminder that when *you* become restless, *you* shall break its yoke from your neck. You shall break free from the bondage and control that food has over you. You shall do that through the freedom found in Christ, His power working inside of you, and by daily choosing to serve Him instead of your flesh.

Prayer

Father, thank You for the freedom that I have in Christ. In Him, I have the power and authority to break the yoke of gluttony. I am free and am no longer a slave to sin. In Jesus' Name, Amen.

Day 12

What's Your Favorite Fruit

But the fruit of the Spirit is love, joy, peace, long-suffering, kindness, goodness, faithfulness, gentleness, self-control. Against such there is no law.
Galatians 5:22-23

The Fruit of the Spirit is evidence of our life in Christ and that Holy Spirit is living within us. Just like in nature, the fruit you bear is evidence of what's inside of you. An apple tree will bear apples. An orange tree has no apples *inside* of it, so it must produce oranges. When you have Holy Spirit living in you, you get to produce His good Fruit.

Unlike a natural tree though, we can bear *all* the Fruit. We don't have to pick just one. Not only do we get to have more self-control, or self-discipline, to help us in our health and freedom journeys, but we get to have the other Fruit too. We get to live lives full of love, joy, and peace. We get to feel less anxious and more patient in stressful situations. We can be kind, good, faithful, and gentle with others. We get to enjoy the goodness of all the Fruit of the Spirit.

Prayer

Father, thank You that Holy Spirit resides in me. Show me times in my day or situations that may come up when I get to bear His Fruit. Reveal to me Fruit that I may need to produce more of, so that I can be a better reflection of You. In Jesus' Name, Amen.

Day 13

You Are His

And those who are Christ's have crucified the flesh with its passions and desires. If we live in the Spirit, let us also walk in the Spirit. Galatians 5:24-25

This is the very next verse after the one about the Fruit of the Spirit that we read yesterday. Through this 40 day fast, you have made the decision to crucify your flesh and live in the Spirit. You are not giving into the passions, cravings, lusts, or desires of the flesh. You are walking in the Spirit and displaying more Fruit.

As this verse says, by doing that, you are showing that you are Christ's. You are His. Let that sink in for a minute. *You are His*. Each time that you don't give in to the temptation to overeat, you are choosing Him and declaring that you are His.

Keep going with this fast. He is doing a work in you spiritually, and you're creating a testimony that will encourage others to choose Him daily as well.

<u>Prayer</u>

Father, thank You for choosing me. Remind me of the good work that You are doing in and through me every time I crucify my flesh. As I go throughout each day of the fast, let it be a form of worship to You and a sign that I am choosing You too. In Jesus' Name, Amen.

Day 14

He Lives In You

Or do you not know that your body is the temple of the Holy Spirit who is in you, whom you have from God, and you are not your own? 1 Corinthians 6:19

As believers, we are housing Holy Spirit and walking around with Him inside of us. When I think of my natural temple compared to a brick and mortar one, it makes me think twice about what I do with it. Surely, a congregation is going to make sure the church building is in the best condition possible, so I should make sure mine is too.

I rarely see a church building with trash all over the outside and definitely not on the inside. So I have to ask myself, what trash have I been letting in? The exterior of the temple would probably be painted beautifully with amazing land-scaping out front. Am I adorning my natural one that well? Coming from the building would be sounds of worship and glory to God. Are the words that I'm speaking glorifying Him and representing Him well?

Your body is a temple. Meditate on this verse for a moment and what that means for you. Write in your journal some ways that you can make your temple a better place for Holy Spirit to reside in.

<u>Prayer</u>

Father, thank You that because of Jesus Christ's sacrifice and Holy Spirit living within me I can be in Your presence daily. Show me ways that I can make this temple a more comfortable place for Holy Spirit. In Jesus' Name, Amen.

Day 15

Glorify God with Your Body

For you were bought at a price; therefore glorify God in your body and in your spirit, which are God's. 1 Corinthians 6:20

Not only are our bodies the temple of the Holy Spirit, but they aren't even ours anymore. Jesus paid the price for our body and spirit so that we no longer have to be slaves to sin. We no longer have to give in to the desires of our flesh. We get to walk in freedom and live by the Spirit instead.

Of course, this doesn't mean that you won't ever sin again or won't ever give in to the temptation to overeat. What it does mean is that now you actually are free to choose *Christ Over Cookies*. As difficult as it may seem at times and as strong as those cravings may feel, the power of God within you is stronger. You have the power now to glorify Him with your body.

Prayer

Father, thank You for paying the price for me. This body is no longer mine, it is Yours. Remind me to give You glory with this body in all that I do, including at times when I'm eating. In Jesus' Name, Amen.

Day 16

Gluttony Leads to Poverty

Do not mix with winebibbers,
Or with gluttonous eaters of meat;
For the drunkard and the glutton will come to
poverty,
And drowsiness will clothe a man with rags.
Proverbs 23:20-21

When I looked up the Hebrew word used for gluttonous and glutton here, one of the definitions was *loose morally*. Loose morally would mean having no restraint nor self control, and according to King Solomon, that is going to lead to poverty. He was the wisest man that ever lived or ever will live (1 Kings 3:12), so I suppose he probably knew what he was talking about here too. Being a glutton will lead to poverty.

Looking back over my financial statements, I would have to agree with him. Most of my money was going to food. This wasn't just grocery shopping either. I was spending large sums of money on fast food and restaurant food; food that I would buy just because I wanted it in the moment or just because I didn't feel like cooking that day. I was being loose morally and lacking discipline when it came to eating, and my lack of money was proof of it. My savings account balance was evidence that gluttony was leading me to poverty.

Take a look at your finances today and see if this is true for you too. In the future, recognize when you're making purchases because you're being "loose morally" and make those opportunities for you to save money and calories.

Prayer

Father, thank You for Your wisdom. Continue to show me how gluttony is leading me towards poverty and away from the life of abundance that You have for me. Teach me to be a better steward over the money You've given me and that I'm saving. In Jesus' Name, Amen.

Day 17

Bless This Meal

For every creature of God is good, and nothing is to be refused if it is received with thanksgiving; for it is sanctified by the word of God and prayer. 1 Timothy 4:4-5

There is so much conflicting and overwhelming advice out there about what you should and shouldn't eat. We've even been warned about the dangers of drinking too much water. Diets range from high carb, low carb, vegan, vegetarian, pescatarian, flexitarian, pegan, carnivore, and whatever else is out there that they come up with tomorrow.

Let this be the verse that eases your mind about what foods to eat. When you look at other translations of it, you'll see that it means every *thing* God created not just every *creature* (animal). Keep this verse in mind when filtering through the information that's out there. Also read 1 Timothy 4:1-3 that comes before this verse. It may be eye opening for you.

Pray and ask the Lord to lead you to what you should and shouldn't eat. Then rest assured that whatever you eat, as long as you pray over it and receive it with thanksgiving, will be sanctified.

Prayer

Father, thank You that everything You create is good. Lead me to the foods that You know will nourish my body best. As I pray over each meal, sanctify it by Your Word. In Jesus' Name, Amen.

Day 18

Strengthen Your Spirit

For bodily exercise profits a little, but godliness is profitable for all things, having promise of the life that now is and of that which is to come. 1 Timothy 4:8

Don't get too excited. Apostle Paul is not giving us a free pass on exercising. Trust me, I'd be one of the first ones to take it. He is just reminding us here of what you've been learning in this book. It's more beneficial for you to strengthen your spirit than to strengthen your body. Focus on the spiritual things, not the things of the flesh.

Your body is temporary. Even if you somehow manage to create the exact body you want, it won't last. However, your spirit will. Your spirit will be beneficial now and in the life to come. Focus on exercising godliness more than exercising your glutes.

<u>Prayer</u>

Father, thank You for the life that is and the life that is to come. As I exercise and make my physical body healthier, remind me of the importance of working out my spiritual one. In Jesus' Name, Amen.

Day 19

You're High Value

Charm is *deceitful and beauty* is *passing,*
But a woman who *fears the Lord, she shall be*
praised. Proverbs 31:30

Just like Apostle Paul wasn't giving us a get out of the gym free card, this verse isn't saying that we get to walk around in leggings all day either. Remember, we have to care about how we adorn our temples.

Like yesterday, it's a reminder that while you should groom yourself, practice good hygiene, and dress in colors, styles, and cuts that look great on you, that isn't what matters most. Your heart posture and reverence for the Lord is.

The Proverbs 31 woman is valued far above rubies. Her value comes from how she stewards the assignments the Lord has given her and how she takes care of the people that He has placed in her life. Her worth has nothing to do with her outer appearance or the size of her dress. Neither does yours.

<u>Prayer</u>

Father, thank You for seeing the value in me. Open my eyes so that I can see it too. In Jesus' Name, Amen.

Day 20

You're Full of It

Remove falsehood and lies far from me;
Give me neither poverty nor riches—
Feed me with the food allotted to me;
Lest I be full and deny You,
And say, "Who is the Lord?"
Or lest I be poor and steal,
And profane the name of my God. Proverbs 30:8-9

It's interesting that Agur, the writer of this Proverb, recognizes that when he is full of food, he's not full of God. In fact, he says his fullness of the belly may cause him to deny the Lord. We can be so full of food that we no longer crave the One Who gave it to us.

As you are halfway through this 40 day journey of choosing *Christ Over Cookies*, I pray that you are starting to see how the Lord is much more filling than food. I hope you're finding that even though you may have cravings, giving into them will only satisfy you momentarily. Nothing satisfies you completely like He does.

<u>Prayer</u>

Father, thank You for sustaining me and filling me up during this fast. Remind me to always get my fill of You, not of food. In Jesus' Name, Amen.

Day 21

Words > Food

I have treasured the words of His mouth
More than my necessary food. Job 23:12b

What a cool place to be in where you treasure God's Words more than food.

Job isn't even talking about loving God's Word more than the treats or extra food like we're learning to do now. This is deeper. He is talking about his *necessary* food. He craves to hear from God more than he craves the very food he needs to survive.

I pray that at some point after you learn to choose *Christ Over Cookies* that you go deeper and start learning to treasure God's Words more than any food. Feasting on His word is better than any gourmet meal and will keep you full longer.

<u>Prayer</u>

Father, thank You for Your Word, written and spoken. I will focus on storing up Your Words in my heart and not on foods in my belly. In Jesus' Name, Amen.

Day 22

Be Thirsty

Blessed are those who hunger and thirst for right-
eousness,
For they shall be filled. Matthew 5:6

Jesus is speaking here and He is declaring that you are blessed and will be filled. You!

How do I know He's speaking to you? I know because, in reading this book and going through this devotional, you are proving that you are hungry and thirsty for righteousness. You're declaring to yourself, to food, and to the Lord that you want to do things His way. Each day that you continue the fast, you are presenting your body as a living sacrifice, holy, acceptable to God.

Keep on fueling your faith instead of feeding your face, and for that sister, the Lord will satisfy you.

Prayer

Father, thank You for satisfying me. As I hunger and thirst for more of You and Your ways, continue to fill me up. In Jesus' Name, Amen.

Day 23

Ignorance Isn't Bliss

My people are destroyed for lack of knowledge.
Hosea 4:6a

The Hebrew word used here for destroyed also means *fail* or *perish*. We, as God's people, are failing, perishing, dying, because of lack of knowledge.

By the way, He doesn't just mean because they are ignorant and they don't know what they don't know. When you look at the very next line of this verse, the Lord says that the people have rejected knowledge. Rejected it. So they had an opportunity to learn and do better, but they refused to. They didn't want to hear it.

Today, this may look like what is happening in congregations that continue to ignore the fact that gluttony is a sin and acknowledge the seriousness of it. It could also be a situation where someone is given a warning over and over again about a medical problem on the horizon that they could prevent if they just changed their behavior, but they never do. Kudos sister, that you have chosen to make a change in your life for the better. You are not rejecting the knowledge. You are welcoming it and taking action.

Prayer

Father, thank You for knowledge, wisdom, and under-standing. Make me aware of any way that I may be resistant to change and rejecting knowledge. In Jesus' Name, Amen.

Day 24

Watch Your Mouth

He who guards his mouth preserves his life,
But he who opens wide his lips shall have destruc-
tion. Proverbs 13:3

I know we're talking here about the words we speak, but truth is truth. This verse can apply to eating as well. Guarding your mouth can save your life.

Another term for guard is *watch over*. By watching over what you put in your mouth (what you're eating) and being more intentional about it, you are taking steps to preserve your life. On the other hand, if you continue to open your mouth wide to just about any and everything you please, that will eventually lead to destruction, disease, and death.

Watch your mouth, sister! Be more diligent with the foods that your mouth is open wide to and how often it is open.

Prayer

Father, thank You for a wide variety of food choices. Bring this verse to my mind when I am opening my mouth wide to ones that don't serve Your temple well. In Jesus' Name, Amen.

Day 25

Heart Check

But the Lord said to Samuel, "Do not look at his appearance or at his physical stature, because I have refused him. For the Lord does not see as man sees; for man looks at the outward appearance, but the Lord looks at the heart." 1 Samuel 16:7

I haven't asked you this yet, why do you want to lose weight? Why do you want to lose weight, *really*?

On the surface it seems great that you want to lose weight, because you *should* want to get healthier. You *should* want to honor God with your body. Is that the real reason for you though?

Take a moment today and journal what's really on your heart. Be real with yourself and God. He already knows anyway. If you find that some of the reasons you want to lose weight are rooted in pride, then now's your time to dig those up. If I'm honest, some of my reasons were too. Repent and ask the Lord to help you go deeper. Turn this journey into one that's about serving Him instead of trying to fit into the world's standard of beauty (or those tight jeans you keep hanging on to).

You can use the 4 S's or R.E.N.E.W. worksheets for this one if you need to. Download them at ChristOverCookies.com /extras.

Prayer

Father, thank You that the condition of my heart is what's most important to You. Lord, I repent of wanting to lose weight for prideful reasons. Let this health journey be one that honors You. In Jesus' Name, Amen.

Day 26

The Land of Contentment

Not that I speak in regard to need, for I have learned in whatever state I am, to be content: I know how to be abased, and I know how to abound. Everywhere and in all things I have learned both to be full and to be hungry, both to abound and to suffer need. I can do all things through Christ who strengthens me. Philippians 4:11-13

Contentment. What a peaceful place to be in!

When you're content, you're not striving. You're not anxious nor wanting more. You are just happy with what is, at that moment. Paul knew how to be content whether he was living humbly or was prosperous, whether his belly was full or he was hungry, whether he was living in need or in overflow. We can learn to be content with just enough and not feel the pressure to overindulge or overstuff ourselves. How do we do it though?

The secret to Paul achieving contentment is in the last verse. He does it through Christ who strengthens him. It's not by his own power or might. It won't be by yours either. You can only get to this place through Christ. As you continue to choose Christ and learn to be satisfied and filled with Him, you'll find that you'll be in this peaceful place too and are content in every season.

Prayer

Father, thank You that it is Christ who strengthens me. If I start leaving the place of contentment, guide me back to finding fulfillment and satisfaction in You. In Jesus' Name, Amen.

Day 27

Enough

O God, You are my God;
Early will I seek You;
My soul thirsts for You;
My flesh longs for You
In a dry and thirsty land
Where there is no water. Psalm 63:1

David wrote this while he was out in the wilderness. I can imagine that he would be hungry and thirsty out there. He even says it's a dry land with no water. Instead of searching for food and water though, David praises God and says that he is hungry and thirsty for Him.

My first time in a group coaching program, my coach asked a strange question, is God enough? My knee jerk response as a daughter of the King is yes! After sitting with that question for days though, I could see areas in my life where the evidence showed that I didn't really believe that He was.

I have the same question for you. Is God enough? If you were stuck in the wilderness, would your first response be to hunger and thirst for *Him*?

Prayer

Father, thank You that You are enough for me. Reveal to me the wilderness places in my life where I am not believing that You are. Help my unbelief. In Jesus' Name, Amen.

Day 28

A Sweet Treat

How sweet are Your words to my taste,
Sweeter than honey to my mouth! Psalm 119:103

Wow! The writer of this Psalm describes God's Word as sweet. Sweeter than honey even. I've learned to get full on God's word while I'm fasting, but I haven't quite gotten to this level yet. I pray that your taste buds get to experience the sweetness of God's Words.

As you are being fed spiritually during this fast, take notes in your journal of how satisfied you feel. Praise God for times when you've had a craving for a sweet, but when you turned to Him you noticed that craving went away.

Prayer

Father, thank You for Your sweet Word. When I have a craving for sweets but I turn to Your Word instead, let it be sweeter than any treat to my mouth. In Jesus' Name, Amen.

Day 29

To God Be The Glory

Therefore, whether you eat or drink, or whatever you do, do all to the glory of God. 1 Corinthians 10:31

Whatever you do, glorify God in doing it. It doesn't matter if you're eating a piece of pie, drinking wine, or hanging out with friends, make sure that you are glorifying God when you do.

This is an easy verse for Holy Spirit to bring to our remembrance to test if what we are doing is acceptable to God. Would it be glorifying God for me to inhale this third piece of sweet potato pie? Would having the third glass of wine be to the glory of God? Is God being glorified in the conversation that I'm having right now with my friends?

Whatever it is that you are doing at home, at work, or when that driver cuts you off in traffic, do it to the glory of God. (Someone needed that driving example.)

<u>Prayer</u>

Father, thank You for this day. As I go throughout my day, make me aware of anything that I'm doing that is not giving You glory. In Jesus' Name, Amen.

Day 30

Intellectual Assent

'And you shall love the Lord your God with all your heart, with all your soul, with all your mind, and with all your strength.' This is the first commandment. Mark 12:30

Intellectual assent is when something goes from head knowledge to heart knowledge. When you don't just know it intellectually, but you know it in your heart too.

For example, you know in your head that a chair is supposed to be able to hold your weight, but you don't truly know it in your heart until you sit in that chair and see that it supports you and doesn't break.

Going through this fast and living spirit-led is getting you to a place where you know God and love Him not just in your head but with all of your heart. You won't just have knowledge of Him. You won't just love Him on a surface level. You are getting to know and love Him intimately. Deeply. When you get to this level, you've just started scratching the surface of how deeply He loves you too.

Prayer

Father, thank You for loving me so much. Take me deeper into our relationship so that I can know You on levels that I never have before. In Jesus' Name, Amen.

Day 31

Help Yourself

All things are lawful for me, but all things are not helpful. All things are lawful for me, but I will not be brought under the power of any. 1 Corinthians 6:12

Let's take a look at the first part of this verse. We'll talk about the second half tomorrow. Apostle Paul is telling us that we can do anything, but everything is not beneficial for us. You can eat anything that you want, but it doesn't mean that it's all helpful for you.

I primarily lose weight through working with a calorie deficit. I can eat *anything* I want. As long as I'm using up more calories than I'm consuming, then I should lose weight. Technically, that would mean that I could eat all of my calories in ice cream, and if I'm still in a deficit then I should lose weight. I may be able to do that, but it doesn't mean that I should. It may be lawful for me, but it's not helpful for me. I wouldn't be serving my body well. Chances are I would feel awful after doing it too. I wouldn't be giving God glory by doing it either.

Remember that just because you *can* have something doesn't necessarily mean that you *should*.

Prayer

Father, thank You that all food is lawful for me. Guide me to the food choices that You know will be most helpful for my body. In Jesus' Name, Amen.

Day 32

I've Got the Power

All things are lawful for me, but all things are not helpful. All things are lawful for me, but I will not be brought under the power of any. 1 Corinthians 6:12

We can eat all things, but we are not to be brought under the power of any. It sounds funny when you actually think about it. How can food, an inanimate object, have control over us? We are powerful, intellectual beings. Yet it can and it does, if we let it.

When I first started my weight loss journey, I knew I needed to stop drinking so much soda. I would drink all soda and no water. That was not helpful for my body. Similar to what you're doing on this fast, I decided to give up soda for a period of time. I told my son that whenever we go to the store not to let me get it. The next time we went to the store I tried to grab it, but he wouldn't let me get it. I started whining and convincing him that I would start again tomorrow, but he wouldn't let me get the soda. I broke down and started crying right in that store. It was at that moment that I realized how much power and control food had over me. It shouldn't be this way. Take your power back sister.

Prayer

Father, thank You for the power and authority You have given me. Show me when I've given that power away and give me the strength to take it back. In Jesus' Name, Amen.

Day 33

A Pizza Drought

And it will be that you shall drink from the brook, and I have commanded the ravens to feed you there. 1 Kings 17:4

There were times when I would be convinced that I had to overstuff myself. I had to have another piece of pizza, even though I was stuffed, because who knows when I would have it again. It's almost as if I was allowing the enemy to convince me to believe that there would be a shortage of pizza the very next day and that I couldn't ever get more. Usually, I would have pizza again the very next week. There was no pizza shortage or need to overstuff myself.

A drought was coming to the land, so God told Elijah to go live near a brook and that He was going to provide for him there. If God has the power to command a stingy bird to bring food to someone during a drought, then why do I ever question His power to provide for me? Why do I feel like I have to hoard food in my belly because of a potential pizza drought?

Don't allow the enemy to use this trick on you to get you to overeat. God can provide during a drought, a shortage, and even a recession. Believe that He will provide what is necessary. The food will be there tomorrow for you. And the next day. And the next.

Prayer

Father, thank You that You are my Source. Show me that You will make sure that I have all the resources that I need and I will not be in lack. In Jesus' Name, Amen.

Day 34

Nourishment through Obedience

So she went away and did according to the word of Elijah; and she and he and her household ate for many days. 1 Kings 17:15

Later in the story we read that the Lord told Elijah to leave the brook. God was going to now provide food and drink for Elijah through a widow. The widow and her son were near death and didn't have enough food to live for another week. In fact, she only had enough food to prepare one last meal. At the request of the prophet though, she decided to be obedient to God and give him her last meal. However, it wasn't her last meal.

She was willing to deny her flesh and hunger and obey the Lord. Because of her obedience, she was provided with more than enough to sustain her, her son, and the prophet for many days. This is a beautiful picture of what you're doing when you choose *Christ Over Cookies*. You are willing to deny your flesh to be obedient to the Lord. You are learning to desire Him and obedience to Him more than you desire food. He will reward you greatly for that.

<u>Prayer</u>

Father, thank You for nourishing me. Continue to satisfy me through Your Word. In Jesus' Name, Amen.

Day 35

Receive Your Crown

Blessed is the man who endures temptation; for when he has been approved, he will receive the crown of life which the Lord has promised to those who love Him. James 1:12

My pastor would tell us that we should consider it a blessing when we have challenges to overcome. We can't be called an overcomer if we haven't overcome anything.

Being overweight and being weighed down by it, doesn't feel like a blessing. Struggling with temptations to overeat or overindulge on sweets, doesn't feel like a blessing. Yet, through my weight loss journey, I've grown closer to Christ and have learned how to help others who struggle with this too. That *is* a blessing. Every time that you don't give in to the temptation and you turn to Christ instead, that is a blessing. You are showing yourself approved. You are showing that you're an overcomer and are worthy to receive the crown. It looks good on you, sis.

Prayer

Father, thank You for making me an overcomer. I know that I will need to continue to endure but I also know that in Christ I can do all things. In Jesus' Name, Amen.

Day 36

Run Your Race

Do you not know that those who run in a race all run, but one receives the prize? Run in such a way that you may obtain it. And everyone who competes for the prize is temperate in all things. Now they do it to obtain a perishable crown, but we for an imperishable crown. Therefore I run thus: not with uncertainty. Thus I fight: not as one who beats the air. But I discipline my body and bring it into subjection, lest, when I have preached to others, I myself should become disqualified. 1 Corinthians 9:24-27

This weight loss journey can feel like a race. A long one. Luckily, we're only running against ourselves.

It doesn't matter how fast or slow it takes anyone else to get to their finish line. You just keep pressing toward *your* mark. Don't look to the right or to the left. Don't allow the enemy to make you feel shame for how long it's taking you to "finally" lose weight. Don't worry that it's taking you two months to lose the same amount of weight that took someone else two weeks to lose. That's their prize, not yours.

Stay in your lane and keep running forward. Keep your eyes focused on Him and the imperishable crown that He has waiting for you.

Prayer

Father, thank You that *my* race is for *me* to run. Help me to be able to celebrate others without falling into the comparison trap. Remind me that my worth and value comes from You. In Jesus' Name, Amen.

Day 37

It's Just Temporary

So God created man in His own image; in the image of God He created him; male and female He created them. Genesis 1:27

When you complete this book and put it away, I pray that Holy Spirit continues to remind you that you are not just your body. You are so much more than that.

You are made in the very image and likeness of God. Don't allow the "realness" of your physical flesh and the world make you forget that. Your body is temporary and will pass away. There is a greater part of you that will continue to live on. The more work you do towards becoming more like Christ, the more your physical body will be influenced by that work as well.

Prayer

Father, thank You for making me in Your image and likeness. When I begin to focus on the temporal things, point me back to what matters most. In Jesus' Name, Amen.

Day 38

Battle Royale

*For the good that I will to do, I do not do; but the
evil I will not to do, that I practice. Romans 7:19*

Remember that the battle between your flesh and spirit is going to be ongoing and not just when it comes to food either. Don't try to rely on willpower or your own might. You know where your strength comes from now. You are equipped to go into battle.

Make sure to keep a journal throughout your weight loss journey. Jot down times when you may be tempted to give in to the desires of the flesh, but by the spirit, you were able to overcome. If your flesh happened to win out, then write why you think it did and what you can do differently next time. You may not be victorious in every battle, but you have already won this war!

<u>Prayer</u>

Father, thank You that the war is already won. Help me to continue to present my body as a living sacrifice to You. In Jesus' Name, Amen.

Day 39

Take Up Your Cross

Then Jesus said to His disciples, "If anyone desires to come after Me, let him deny himself, and take up his cross, and follow Me. Matthew 16:24

You have proven over the last 38 days that you desire to go after Christ. You denied yourself, became a living sacrifice, and followed Him. Don't let this pursuit of Christ end after the 40 days are completed. Be intentional about continuing to deny yourself and take up your cross.

The enemy is going to try to convince you at times that you aren't free. He's going to try to convince you that the work on the cross was not to free you from the sin of gluttony. Remember that he is a liar. If he's saying it, then the opposite must be true. Continue to walk in your freedom. Show him that you can deny yourself, take up your cross, and that your desire is now for Christ.

Prayer

Father, thank You that I am free in Christ Jesus. In my weakness, let Your power be made perfect and give me strength to continue to walk in freedom. In Jesus' Name, Amen.

Day 40

Complete the Work

*...being confident of this very thing, that He who
has begun a good work in you will complete it until
the day of Jesus Christ. Philippians 1:6*

I don't believe that it's a coincidence that you came across
this book. Whether you felt led to purchase it or someone
gave it to you, it's in your hands for a reason. The Lord
has started doing a work in you through the work you've
done within the pages of this book. He is a faithful God, and
He will complete the good work. Allow Him to do it. Show
others that they can do it too.

Prayer

Father, thank You for the good work that You have begun
in me. My heart and hands are open for You to complete
it. In Jesus' Name, Amen.

Go Forth!

You did it! You completed 40 days of choosing *Christ Over Cookies*. You chose to not have your go-to sweet or food when the carvings hit and to go to Christ instead. Even if you didn't do it for all 40 days, you still made the conscious decision to learn to seek God for satisfaction, not food. *That* is to be celebrated. Three clapping-hands emojis for you!

1. Eryn Sun, Christian Post Reporter. THURSDAY, MARCH 24, 2011. Firm Faith, Fat Body? Study Finds High Rate of Obesity among Religious https://www.christianpost.com/news/firm-faith-fat-body-study-finds-high-rate-of-obesity-among-religious-49568/#Zo7zlJFhsEbBPscP.99

2. Raihan N, Cogburn M. Stages of Change Theory. [Updated 2023 Mar 6]. In: StatPearls [Internet]. Treasure Island (FL): StatPearls Publishing; 2023 Jan-. Available from: https://www.ncbi.nlm.nih.gov/books/NBK556005/

3. Heather Shriver Burns, Master Neuroscience Business & Biblical Life Coach. HeatherShriverBurns.com

RESOURCES

For free resources and worksheets, go to:
ChristOverCookies.com/extras

If you are a woman who wants to lose a significant amount
of weight, join me for free inside of Transformation Tribe:
TransformationTribe.vip

CONNECT WITH MALAIKA

MalaikaBurley.com
YouTube, Facebook, Instagram: @MalaikaBurley
Overweighted Podcast

Email: info@malaikaburley.com

Mailing Address:
Malaika Burley
P.O. Box 32
Palmetto, FL 34220

Printed in Great Britain
by Amazon